The "Successful Life Skills" manual is the epitome of what the recovery movement represents. This guide can direct anyone to learn and improve their lives on a holistic level, focusing on solutions rather than labels or diagnoses. It also focuses on choices which are paramount for people to engage and participate in a learning experience. Kudos to Charles and Ron!

Cynthia Branch, PRS/ICRC, PSS/RSPS, PM/PRC, CHW
Manager of Recovery Support Services
The Council on Recovery

This new manual is by far the easiest, most targeted and user-friendly treatment tool that has come along in forever. It meets the standards for evidence-based treatment, follows a natural progression and can be used in either facilitator-led or participant-led groups. It really gives momentum for participants to get started, get it right, and keep recovery going.

Kevin Minnick, MS LMHC LCAC
Court Treatment Specialist
Hancock County Courts, Indiana

Successful Life Skills is an insightful guide, written in layman's terms, and outlining practical steps to a more productive, successful life. It would be a beneficial read for everyone - the insights into how our minds work are universal.

Focused and thoughtful reading of this book will instill HOPE in people who wish to make changes in their lives and the POWER to make them.

Honorable Sherry Applewhite, JD

Ron Lott and Charles True have upgraded SMART Recovery and NIDA's evidence-based InsideOut Program for the 21st Century, extending the program components and including life skills. The result is a masterpiece!

Joe Gerstein, Founding President of SMART Recovery, MD, FACP, Clin. Asst. Prof. of Medicine, Harvard Medical School (Ret.)

Successful Life Skills
Including SMART Recovery Tools

SMART Recovery®
Self-Management and Recovery Training

Based on the InsideOut program Developed in Collaboration with
the National Institute on Drug Abuse

April 1, 2019

Welcome to SMART Recovery!

This book is based on the SMART Recovery Handbook which is used by thousands of people each week in meetings around the world.

SMART is the world's largest community of peer support groups that uses science-based tools to overcome behaviors that aren't working for us. You will learn how to deal with thinking that gets you into trouble. Things don't just happen to us. We have thoughts that create feelings that lead to behaviors that sometimes work out well and sometimes don't. We will show you where to find the power to replace self-destructive behaviors with a healthier lifestyle.

We believe that you decide what problems, if any, you want to work on and what methods will work best for you.

We don't give advice, we won't tell you what to do or what to believe. We won't require you to label yourself. We'll do our best to ask thought-provoking questions that you and your peers answer. Once you've heard the ideas of others, you decide what's best for you.

This workbook is not like a diet with a long list of restrictions you must follow; it's more like a buffet where you get to choose what you like. When you find something you think will be useful to you, make a note and give it a try.

Ron Lott

Facilitator, Recovery Coach

April 1, 2019

The vision of the Texas SMART Prison Program is to build and present an enrolling and understandable course that is available to anyone in need. Whatever our current incarceration and earlier social and economic status has shown us, our purpose is to have simplified relatable lessons.

Our hope for all of us is that these somewhat personalized and evidence-based skills for recovery can and will strengthen our relatedness to each other, enriching our personal development and growth goals.

The concept that we humans thrive on our rational free will and are capable of choosing more for our lives when we're recognized, engaged and motivated to our higher levels of being is not new.

My personal experience of one of life's bottom lines over the last three decades is that:

Most, if not all, recovery occurs between people, and our best purpose in engaging each other is to create the kind of lives we will not want to relapse from.

I want us all to be addicted to reality.

Charles True

Acknowledgments

Format, editing, and new material by Ron Lott and Charles True who currently reserve all rights for this work.

Special thanks to Albert Ellis whose research has led to most of the tools we use today and to Barry Grant and Bill Greer for editing the most recent Participant Handbook for *Learn SMART InsideOut Fast: A Course for Short-Term Populations* as well.

We also want to acknowledge these people for their large contributions: former SMART Presidents, Tom Horvath and Joe Gerstein; Bill Abbott; Jim Braastad; John Frahm; Rosemary Hardin; Randy Lindel; Richard Lazarus; Stanton Peele; Martin Seligman; Phillip Kendall; George Miller; Terry London; Michael Shear; the Albert Ellis Institute and Chicago Institute for REBT.

Thanks to two people in Texas who lit the torch and have kept it burning in Houston for the last 25 years, Rob Sarmiento and Ruth Fowler.

Thanks to Sandy Lewis, Fred Bender and Carlos Naylor for showing up each week to help teach the course. Their passion for helping others is admirable and we couldn't have reached so many people without their support.

Thanks to Mark Ruth, Christi Alicia, the corporate staff and the entire SMART Recovery community for their limitless support and generosity sharing their ideas, best practices and experiences, especially Judy Carr, Tom Burke, Carol Siddall, Rebecca Genter and Doug Hanshaw.

Thanks to Dr. Joe Gerstein for his passion and encouragement from the idea stage of teaching a course in prison all the way to writing this book.

Special thanks to Warden Kendrick Demyers, Chaplain Tom Lowe, and Chaplain Lunetta Mitchell for approving our program to be taught in TDCJ. Without their support we would not be where we are today.

Extra special thanks to the hundreds of TDCJ offenders who have been through our program. Their honesty, integrity and courage to fully participate in a difficult environment is an inspiration to us every day.

Contents

Introduction

We Bring Science and Reason to Self-Help with Addictive Behaviors

SMART Recovery is a science-based (evidence-based) community of addiction recovery support groups where participants learn self-empowering techniques to aid their recovery through face-to-face and online meetings. We learn from each other. We are a nonprofit organization with well over 3,000 groups meeting weekly around the world, plus more than 30 online meetings a week. Since we are science-based, you have the power to be any religion or none at all and use our tools.

We believe that recovery is complex and there is no *one-size-fits-all* solution. You and only you are in charge of your recovery. You choose what that looks like and the resources/methods you will use to reach your goals. We believe in *therapeutic diversity* and encourage everyone to consider all options including medication-assisted treatment (MAT), faith, 12 step, diet, exercise, peer groups and any other resources available to you.

We teach a series of tools that anyone can use to change the way they *think* and *feel*. We have tools that help you identify where you are in the stages of change. We will help you identify your priorities in life and develop a plan to achieve your goals. You will also learn what a healthy balanced life looks like.

Who is responsible for your behavior and any changes that need to be made?

REBT by Dr. Albert Ellis

Many of the tools we use came from behavioral research conducted by psychologist Albert Ellis.

The diagram on the next page explains the concept of REBT. Simply put, rational refers to what we think. Emotive is what we feel. And behavior represents our actions. We have changed therapy to transformation. Our actions transform our lives, i.e., married/divorced, employee/friend, free/incarcerated. Our thoughts significantly affect the way we feel. Our feelings affect how we act. And our actions affect our results and our satisfaction or dissatisfaction with our lives.

Think back about an event in your life that didn't end well and write it in the box. Next, write down what you were feeling that allowed you to take the action you did. Then, write down what you were thinking that made you feel that way. Last, write down a new thought that will lead to a better outcome for you.

Rational **E**motive **B**ehavior **T**herapy

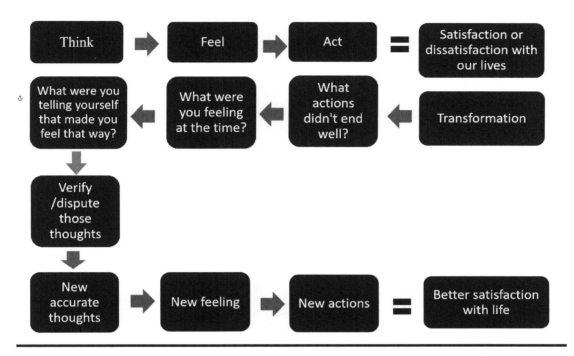

Fill out the example below with a time in your life where your actions didn't turn out well for you. You may want to use the event that got you incarcerated.

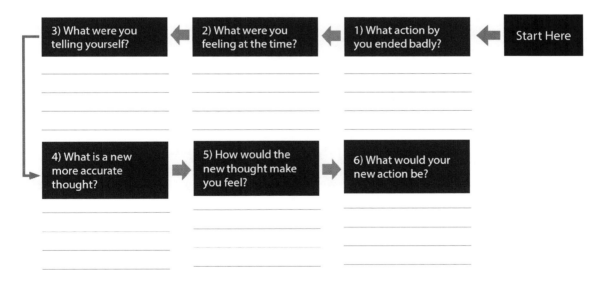

This page intentionally left blank.

Name: _____

Date: _____

Locus of Control Survey

Read the following statements and put a Y in the space if you agree and an N if you disagree with the statement. There are no right or wrong answers. We will return with a summary of the results next week and discuss the implications.

_____1. Do you believe that most problems will solve themselves if you just don't fool with them?

_____2. Do you believe that you can stop yourself from catching a cold?

_____3. Are some people just born lucky?

_____4. Most of the time, do you feel that getting good grades means a lot to you?

_____5. Are you often blamed for things that aren't your fault?

_____6. Do you believe that if somebody studies hard enough, they can pass any subject?

_____7. Do you believe that most of the time it doesn't pay to try hard because things never turn out right anyway?

_____8. Do you feel that if things start out well in the morning that it's going to be a good day no matter what else you do?

_____9. Do you feel that most of the time parents listen to what their children have to say?

_____10. Do you believe that wishing can make good things happen?

_____11. When you get punished does it usually seem it's for no good reason?

_____12. Do you find it's hard to change a friend's opinion about something?

_____13. Do you think that cheering more than others helps a team to win?

_____14. Do you feel that it's nearly impossible to change your parents' mind about anything?

_____15. Do you believe that parents should allow children to make most of their own decisions?

_____16. Do you feel that when you do something wrong, there's very little you can do to make it right?

_____17. Do you believe that most people are just born good at sports?

_____18. Are most of the other people your age stronger than you are?

_____19. Do you feel that one of the best ways to handle most problems is to just not think about them?

_____20. Do you feel that you have a lot of choice in deciding who your friends are?

Fold and tear here

____21. If you found a 4-leaf clover, do you believe that it might bring you good luck?

____22. Do you often feel that whether or not you do your homework has little to do with the grades you get?

____23. Do you feel that when someone is angry at you, there is little you can do to stop them?

____24. Have you ever had a good luck charm?

____25. Do you believe that whether or not people like you depends on how you act?

____26. Do your parents usually help you if you ask them to?

____27. Have you felt that when someone is angry with you it is usually for no reason at all?

____28. Do you feel that you can change what might happen tomorrow by what you do today?

____29. Do you feel that when bad things are going to happen, they are just going to happen no matter what you do to try to stop them?

____30. Do you feel that people can get their own way if they just keep trying?

____31. Most of the time, do you find it useless to try to get your own way at home?

____32. Do you feel that when good things happen, they happen because of hard work?

____33. Do you feel that when someone wants to be your enemy, there is little you can do to change their mind?

____34. Do you feel that it's easy to get friends to do what you want them to do?

____35. Do you feel that you have little to say about what you get to eat at home?

____36. Do you feel that when someone doesn't like you, there is little you can do about it?

____37. Do you feel that it's useless to try hard at work or school because other people are just plain smarter than you?

____38. Do you believe that planning ahead makes things turn out better?

____39. Do you feel that you usually have little to say about what your family decides to do?

____40. Do you feel that it's better to be smart than lucky?

Fold and tear here

Locus of Control

Locus of Control is a model for how much control people feel that they have over things that impact their lives.

Think back over the challenges in your life and consider whether your decisions were based on something inside of you or outside of you that ultimately determined the outcome. Were they really your choice, or do you believe that you were simply left to the devices of something (or someone) outside of you?

When you believe that you have ultimate control over what happens, then you have what psychologists refer to as an internal locus of control. If you believe that you have no control over what happens and that external forces are to blame, then you have what is known as an external locus of control.

Your locus of control views have power to influence not only how you respond to the events that happen in your life, but also how *motivated* you are to take action. If you believe that you hold the keys to your fate, you are more likely to take action to change your situation when needed. If, on the other hand, you believe that the outcome is out of your hands, you may be less likely to work toward change.

Those with an internal locus of control:

- Are more likely to take responsibility for their actions.
- Tend to be less influenced by the opinions of others.
- Often do better at tasks when they are allowed to work on their own.
- Tend to work hard to achieve the things they want.
- Feel confident in the face of challenges.
- Report being happier and more independent.
- Often achieve better success in the workplace.

Those with an external locus of control:

- Blame outside forces for their circumstances.
- Often blame luck or chance for any success.
- Don't believe they can change their situation through their own efforts.
- Frequently feel hopeless or powerless in the face of difficult situations.
- Are more prone to experience learned helplessness or they just give up.

Do you have an internal or external locus of control?

Which of these statements best describes your outlook on life?

1) I often feel that I have little control over my life and what happens to me. People rarely get what they deserve. It isn't worth setting goals or making plans because too many things can happen that are outside of my control. Life is a game of chance; individuals have little influence over events in the world.

2) If you work hard and commit yourself to a goal you can achieve anything. There is no such thing as fate or destiny. If you study hard and are well prepared, you can do well on exams. Luck has little to do with success; it's mostly a matter of dedication and effort. In the long run, people tend to get what they deserve in life.

Neither of these are absolutely RIGHT. It is important for you to know where you stand if you want to stay there.

Thought to remember

If you have an internal locus of control, it means that you believe that your actions have an impact on your life. That can give you the motivation you need to change.

If you tend to have a more external locus of control, you might find it helpful to start actively trying to change how you view situations and events. Rather than viewing yourself as a passive bystander who is caught up in the flow of life, think about actions you can take that will have a positive impact on your outcomes.

"If words control you that means that everyone else can control you. Breathe and allow things to pass."
—Bruce Lee

Do you have more internal or external Locus of Control?

_____

Give some examples of your thoughts and actions to back up your opinion.

_____
_____
_____
_____

How can you develop more of an internal Locus of Control?

_____
_____
_____
_____

What is your opinion of this concept?

_____

If you refer to a person by saying, "He don't take no shit off nobody!" what does that say about his Locus of Control? Is he more internal or external?

_____

_____

There is a key to score your LOC survey in the appendix on page (111).

The Hula Hoop Theory

Once you begin to develop a more internal LOC and realize that you do have control over your own life, the Hula Hoop Theory will also make sense.

Start by placing a Hula Hoop on the ground and step inside of it. The circle around you represents the space that you have control over in this world. LOC tells us that you can control what goes on in your life and the Hula Hoop Theory says that you cannot control anything outside of it.

"You do not have the moral authority or ability to control anyone else."

Yes, that includes the people closest to you. You may succeed in controlling them for a moment by intimidating them with your size or by withholding money or affection, but what happens when you leave the room?

_____

_____

How does it make you feel when you try to control someone else? Powerful, frustrated, angry?

_____

_____

"I have found that managing what goes on inside my Hula Hoop is a full time job. I don't have the time or energy to manage anyone else."

What do you think about that statement?

_____

_____

_____

_____

Cost Benefit Analysis

On the next page is our Cost Benefit Analysis. Start by filling in a substance or activity that you believe may be causing you problems. Then, list all of the benefits to you that you can think of for using the substance or activity (yes, there are benefits to illegal drugs, or you wouldn't be using them).

Then fill in the costs or drawbacks of using or doing those substances or activities. They don't have to match or have the same number of benefits and costs.

Below that, list all the benefits and costs of NOT doing those things. If you think about it, you will discover that it's not just the reverse of the list above.

Cost Benefit Analysis Chart

The substance or activity to consider is: _____

Date _____

Using or Doing (Label each item short-term (ST) or long-term (LT))	
Benefits (rewards and advantages)	**Costs** (risks and disadvantages)

NOT Using or Doing (Label each item short-term (ST) or long-term (LT))	
Benefits (rewards and advantages)	**Costs** (risks and disadvantages)

Short and Long-term benefits

Once you have completed your list of costs and benefits, go back and label each item (ST) if its short-term or (LT) if it's long-term.

What patterns do you see?

_____

_____

_____

_____

Once you see your patterns, what do they mean to you?

_____

_____

_____

_____

The benefits of using alcohol, drugs and other harmful behaviors are usually short term.

The costs of our destructive behavior (e.g. lost relationships, financial losses, being arrested) are more often long term.

SMART Defined

Self-Management and Recovery Training

Self—The self is an awakened sense of who you are as a person with a unique personality that bases decisions on experiences, beliefs, observations and perceived wants and needs. The Self is an empowered and individually motivated person who *is not defined* by what others think or try to label. It is who you know yourself to be at the deepest level and what you rise to become.

Management—Having the ability to handle the important aspects of your life with a realistic degree of balanced reason and rationality.

What's important for you to learn to manage and why?

If you have thought about who you are and who you are not, there are probably some areas that appear to be in need of adjusting—or "managing" in a different way. You may have chosen to believe that your decision-making was based upon what you experienced through peer pressure, or being ridiculed at some time in your life was the reason for using or choosing a "street lifestyle."

What does it mean to you?

Managing your life means arranging, or putting into the order of importance, healthy life choices and making every reasonable effort to manage those choices.

Recovery—The ongoing process of not using addictive substances or indulging in self-defeating behaviors, and learning and practicing the awareness and skills necessary to live a whole, healthy, and healed life.

What are you recovering from?

You are recovering from the false beliefs and distorted ways in which you chose to see the life you were leading. Perhaps you were told you were not good enough, or you believe or *told yourself* that it's okay to undervalue life by drinking or using drugs. Although these are challenging issues and no one would choose to "experience" or live through these conditions, you have done so and they are yours to own—and they are also yours from which you have a choice to recover.

What are you recovering from?

_____

_____

_____

_____

What, if anything, are you trying to recover?

It is a recovery of who you knew in your innocence of mind, before the disturbing reality that life is not the wonderful experience that you thought it was. It is a recovery of your Self before the attraction to use drugs, or the appeal of excitement provided by the street's negative energy, or the many faces that glorify a false world of power, recognition and worth. It is a recovery of your true self and everything that you already were.

What do you wish to recover?

_____

_____

_____

_____

Should we be trying to get back something lost or creating something new?

_____

_____

What Is Addictive Behavior?

In order to change using the SMART Recovery program, it is helpful to have a good understanding of addictive behavior. Key points:

A good definition of addiction is "poor self-control over behaviors that seek pleasure or reward but also cause harm."

If you find it hard to stop doing something that causes long-term harm, this might be an addictive behavior.

If you find yourself doing a behavior to keep from getting sick rather than for fun, you're probably addicted.

Addictive behavior does not just include using substances. Such behaviors can also include activities such as overeating, drug dealing, gambling, video games, spending, robbery, car thefts, running cons, scams and bullying.

We all know what this looks like—people doing the same things again and again that are obviously self-destructive, even if they repeatedly try to stop. Addictive behaviors usually start out as a pleasurable habit that is easy to control. Over time, the desire to engage in the behavior grows stronger and stronger—even though the pleasure or fun of the early days is no longer there.

Which definition of addictive behavior do you relate to most?

_____

_____

_____

The Problem of Instant Gratification (PIG)

As it gets harder to control the behavior, we rely on short-term thinking to tell ourselves that we must continue to use. To other people, it is obvious that the addictive behavior is causing lots of long-term problems. The addicted person pays attention only to the immediate benefits, such as pleasure, feeling normal or relieving withdrawal symptoms, and gives in to the need for "instant gratification." We describe this as the Problem of Instant Gratification or the PIG. Each time we give in to an urge, the Pig grows bigger and gets hungrier. Our urges become more powerful and come more often. We need more of the same behavior just to feel normal and get through the day.

The good news is that you can put the Pig on a diet and it will slim down! If you refuse to give in to urges, they will get smaller and bother you less. Fewer things will trigger your urges and the Pig will become less of a problem in your life.

Alert!!!! A recent study (2018) found that the opioid overdose *death rate was 39 times greater* among formerly incarcerated people for the first two weeks after release than in the general population. Why?

_____
_____
_____
_____

List any behaviors you have that you feel might be addictive.

_____
_____
_____
_____

What is the problem with instant gratification?

_____
_____
_____
_____

How SMART Recovery Works

SMART Recovery helps you find the power and motivation within to replace self-destructive behavior with a healthy lifestyle. You reconnect with your most important values and create change plans to lead a balanced, fulfilling and meaningful life.

SMART stands for Self-Management and Recovery Training, reflecting its focus on helping you make positive life changes. Addictive behavior is more than drinking and using other drugs; it includes criminal thinking, gambling, conning and manipulation. All of these have to do with how you are thinking, or really not thinking, about your long-term well-being.

SMART shows you how to deal with thinking that gets you into trouble. First you work on changing your thinking. You learn to see problems before they happen, improve how you communicate with others, and stay away from alcohol and drugs. You also learn why it's important to stay away from the lifestyle that helped create a lot of your problems.

Our brains are constantly rewiring our automatic thoughts based on our experiences. You taught yourself bad habits by doing the same things over and over. Your thinking patterns can be changed in a positive way by doing the exercises in this book and repeating them. Your brain automatically tells you not to touch a hot stove or to stay away from snakes. You can re-learn to automatically stay away from harmful activities in the same way by repeating exercises and routines that have a different outcome. Let's say there was a gas station near your work where you used to get a beer for the drive home. As soon as you saw the sign you began to think of the cold drink going down your throat. After doing the Cost-Benefit Analysis you have decided that the costs outweigh the benefits of having that beer. Every time you drive by that station without stopping you are re-wiring your brain to a new normal behavior.

What, if anything, about how SMART works makes sense to you?

_____

_____

_____

_____

Believe it, you CAN change!

According to a 2002 NESARC study, 75% of Americans with alcohol addiction quit on their own without ever receiving any form of treatment or attending even one meeting. So the odds are 3:1 that you will quit, the only question is when and how much more damage will you do to yourself and others before you quit?

It's important that you believe in your own ability to change.

Don't fall into the self-fulfilling prophecy trap.

Failing to change only proves that you have not yet mastered the skills or become motivated to change.

Change is usually difficult but not impossible, 75% of us do it on our own!

Change is a process not an event.

Setbacks are *learning experiences* not proof of failure.

Give an example of something you learned to do that developed into automatic thinking.

_____

_____

How is it possible to learn to think the opposite thoughts about something?

_____

_____

_____

_____

Joke for the day: Do you know how many therapists it takes to change a lightbulb?

One...but the lightbulb has to want to change!

What is the chance of someone being successful from going to treatment if they don't want to change?

_____

_____

Do you believe you have the power to make changes in your life? Answer and explain why.

_____

_____

_____

What is the difference between

Treatment and Recovery?

Recovery Definition: A process of change through which individuals improve their health and wellness, live self-directed lives and strive to reach their full potential. Recovery is based on access to recovery capital and the inspiration to make positive changes. There are four parts of recovery that you'll want to consider:

HOME: A stable and safe place to live.

PURPOSE: Meaningful daily activities—job, school, care taking, volunteering, having the income and resources to participate in society.

COMMUNITY: Relationships and social networks that provide support, friendship, love and hope.

HEALTH: Overcoming or managing one's diagnosis or symptoms and making informed, healthy choices that support physical and mental well-being.

Treatment Definition: The techniques or actions applied to a specific situation.

Treatment addresses a specific need where recovery <u>includes for all aspects of your life.</u> In this book we will address as many of those as we can. You decide which ones are important to you to achieve your goals in life.

What is the difference between treatment and recovery?

_____

_____

_____

Which is more important to you, treatment or recovery?

_____

_____

_____

Recovery Capital

Recovery Capital consists of the assets that you as an individual possess to aid you in your recovery. Circle the ones that you will have when released and add any additional ones that you can think of.

PHYSICAL: Health, money, car insurance, health insurance, driver's license, place to live, transportation, tools,

_____

_____

_____

HUMAN: Hope, skills, trade, legal status, bilingual, certifications, education, degrees, knowledge, sense of purpose,

_____

_____

_____

SOCIAL: Relationships, family, friends, church, neighbors, classmates, co-workers, sports leagues, peer groups, clubs,

_____

_____

_____

Why is it important for you to make this list?

1) It is encouraging. Most people have more than they realize.

2) It points out what you don't have and need to get.

3) These are your assets; you should protect all of them just like you do your money.

4)_____

5)_____

The SMART 4-Point Program®

SMART features a practical 4-Point Program that teaches you the skills and provides a framework to overcome addictive, self-defeating behavior.

Point 1: Enhancing and Maintaining Motivation

This point simply asks: "Why do you want to or think you need change?" It asks you to consider the costs and the benefits of your addictive behavior. The motivation must come from within. You must decide to change for reasons that make sense to you and to follow a course of action to sustain that change with practices that work for you.

Point 2: Coping with Urges

Here you identify and challenge the belief that you really must take part in a certain behavior just because the thought or feeling comes up—without giving thought to the negative consequences. You will learn techniques for coping with and strategies to avoid urges.

Point 3: Managing Thoughts, Feelings and Behaviors

It is important for you to understand that thinking can be an automatic and habitual reaction, and for that reason it is important to change how you see yourself, the person next to you, and the world in which you are living. It helps you to **know that YOU have a choice**. You may not be able to change other people or the world, but you have a choice to change yourself and learn how to interact more effectively and not be distracted by things you cannot change.

Point 4: Lifestyle Balance

This point teaches you how to have a lifestyle that is healthy and balanced. You will also learn skills to prevent relapses and to rebuild the quality person you left behind, before you chose the negative over the positive. These skills include recognizing triggers and high-risk situations as you construct a new way of living.

Whether you want to overcome addictive or compulsive behavior or substance use problems, SMART has information, tools, and techniques that have power to help you replace your self-destructive behaviors with healthier options. It offers more than just a means to stop harmful practices; SMART presents ways to transform yourself with a new lifestyle and a balanced, fulfilling and meaningful life—whatever that means to you.

Do you have any addictive behaviors other than alcohol or drugs? If so, list them:

_____

_____

If there are going to be changes in your life, who will be responsible?

_____

_____

_____

_____

Which of the four points is most important to you and why?

_____

_____

_____

Point 1—Building Motivation to Change

Let's start by looking at why you might want to consider changing the way you think or the things that you do. To not change when change is necessary is destructive. The question of why to change is no longer something that just family or friends ask, but in those quiet moments you probably have asked yourself.

The answer is not in this course; it is within you. In order to change, you need to think about what you really want, and take an honest look at how your addictive behaviors have affected your life. Most of your big problems are the result of choices you have made, which is good news because it means you can do something about them.

Key Points:

Some things matter to us more than other things.

Sometimes you do things that undermine what is most important to you.

This is self-defeating and painful. You cannot keep doing this and also be happy.

Thinking about what you want in the future is a good way to motivate yourself on your recovery journey.

In order to lead a healthy, fulfilling and balanced life—something most everyone wants—you start like anything else, by making a plan. As illustrated in the following worksheets, start by setting a goal and asking three questions: What do you want for your future? How can you achieve that? How do you feel about what you are currently doing—or not doing—in order to reach that goal?

In the following worksheet, figure out all the details you have to cover in order to succeed. This will require some thought and hard work due to the fact that you want to be specific. You might want to make change plans for different parts of your life. For example, how will you stop using drugs? How will you develop a new lifestyle without drugs and with healthy and fulfilling activities you like? How will you find a job to support your life and your family? How will you find the job of your dreams? Be ambitious. Challenge yourself.

A Course for Successful Life Skills

Throughout this course, you can work on these plans as you learn more about the changes needed and how you want to improve yourself and become the person you want to be. You might keep refining and improving your plans throughout this book. You will discover new skills and interests and opportunities that arise.

Life is Change,
Growth is optional,
Choose Wisely!

—Albert Einstein

Stages of Change

V. Maintenance: The positive changes I've made in my behavior are now my automatic thoughts and routine.

IV. Action: I am actively taking steps to make changes in my life.

III. Preparation: I know I need to change and am actively looking into my options to make changes.

II. Contemplation: Maybe I do have a problem but I don't know what to do.

I. Precontemplation: I don't have any problems; no change is needed.

Where do you feel you are today on the Stages of Change path?

_____

_____

_____

Point 1—Building Motivation to Change

Hierarchy of Values

What is your foundation?

First let's consider your position: who you believe you are, and why you are here. Before you got involved in whatever brought you to where you are right now, did your vision include this? A foundation is your base, what you support as your own personal beliefs for a successful life. For example, creating or reestablishing a loving family life or returning to school. Without a solid foundation, you can easily be blown away. Remember, this is your life and you build the foundation from where you *are*, not where you *were*.

What are your Most Important Values?

What about your inner rulebook of feelings that speak to your inside truth—the values that define what is most important in how you lead your life?

What are your most important values?

1) _____

2) _____

3) _____

4) _____

5) _____

If you didn't put substance abuse on your list, where would you put it since it likely conflicts with your other values?

_____

_____

_____

_____

1) What do I want for my future?

_____

_____

_____

_____

2) What am I doing to achieve that?

_____

_____

_____

_____

3) What am I doing to sabotage that?

_____

_____

_____

_____

4) What does a successful life look like to you?

_____

_____

_____

_____

Point 1—Building Motivation to Change

Change-Plan Worksheet

Now that you know what you want for your future and what you need to get there, you need a plan.

Changes I want to make:

_____

_____

_____

_____

How important are these changes? (scale of 1-10, with 10 being the highest)

_____

How confident am I that I can make these changes? (1-10 scale)

_____

Most important reasons to make these changes:

_____

_____

_____

Steps to make the changes:

_____

_____

_____

How other people can help me:

Person	Kind of help

I will know my plan is working when:

_____

_____

_____

Point 2—Learn to Cope with Urges

Okay, so you have taken a look at what you value, considered that in order to grow you probably need to change your thinking, and that leads you into becoming a changed and powerful you. If it was that easy, you probably wouldn't be where you are right now. A large part of continuing the changes that are helping you and re-discovering who you were before using is preparing for the urges and cravings that make it difficult to change.

What is an Urge?

An urge is a strong feeling or desire to engage in a behavior that you had decided not to do. If you are addicted to a behavior, then urges are completely normal. There are four types of urges:

Withdrawal Symptoms: If you are a heavy user of drugs like alcohol, cocaine or heroin, you may experience an urge to use due to the fact that you are physically dependent (addicted); you may have experienced symptoms such as sweatiness, nervousness, sleeplessness and loss of appetite. In this case, the abstinence is creating physical discomfort and suffering. You might need medication to make withdrawal medically safe, but the urges themselves are not dangerous.

Unwanted Mood: Some people get bored, anxious or depressed and then feel an urge to take part in their addictive behavior to instantly improve their mood. For example, when a person whose addictive behavior is gambling feels restless or on edge, they may have the urge to go out to a casino and place a bet, or a person who feels socially anxious might believe an alcoholic drink would relax them, resulting in the urge to drink.

Conditioning: You may have had a favorite place to hang around, and you may have found that no matter what mood you were in, passing that place created an urge to drink/use or take part in a certain behavior. A street corner, a person you used to use with, or a time of day may bring about an urge.

Point 2—Learn to Cope with Urges

Making the Good Even Better: You may have found that taking part in your addictive behavior enhanced an already positive experience. For example, perhaps you thought that sex was better when you were high or a party was more fun when you were intoxicated.

Which of the 4 types of Urges have you experienced? _____

    Describe what it was like, how you felt

_____

_____

_____

What an Urge Is Not

- Excruciating, unbearable or permanent.
- Something that ***makes*** you engage in your addictive behavior. It is a choice you make to go back to the addictive behavior in response to an urge.
- All powerful. While it might feel that way, an urge is not unbearable, permanent or long-lasting, and its power weakens the longer you refrain from using or engaging in addictive behavior.
- Something that is never-ending. Urges will diminish in as few as three to 18 minutes, especially as you start behaving in healthy and fulfilling ways free of addictions.

Strategies for Coping with Urges

The following is a list of strategies that have been proven to be effective in coping with urges.

Think about them and which ones might work for you.

Basic

1) **Avoid**—Stay away from situations, sensations and people that may bring on an urge.
2) **Escape**—If you find yourself in an urge-provoking situation, get out of there immediately.
3) **Distract yourself**—This can be physical or mental. Concentrate on something other than your urge, think of a place you would like to go for vacation, think of someone you really care about and why. Go for a walk, do some chores, do something that changes your heart rate.
4) **Review your CBA**—Get a pen and paper and write it down, don't try to do it in your head where it's competing with your urge.
5) **Recall negative consequences**—What was it like being arrested, notifying your family, being sentenced or walking into the prison for the first time?
6) **Picture your future**—Visualize a time in the near future where you are doing something while sober and are happy about it.
7) **Reach out to someone for support**—Call a friend or family member who is familiar with your new goals and is willing to listen to your thoughts.
8) **Recognize the urge for what it is**, just another of many thoughts in your head. Don't think you have to own it or become it. It's just a thought and like all others, it will pass.
9) **Keep an Urge Log**
10) **Make a Plan for your time**—You may have a lot of extra time to fill once you stop using, make a plan for productive activities during that time.

Advanced

1) Move beyond avoidance—When you are in the early stages of recovery it is wise to avoid all places that are triggers. Once you feel comfortable with your willpower, go to a restaurant that serves alcohol; take a friend who knows your situation. Practice using your basic strategies.
2) Rehearse in your mind how you will handle situations. For example, you have a wedding or a Super Bowl party to go to this weekend. Someone will ask you why you aren't drinking, figure out now what you are going to say and rehearse it.
3) Bring out your urge—After you have developed some confidence in coping with urges, you may want to confront them on your own terms rather than waiting until you are in a situation. Think about a time you had an urge. Visualize how you can deal with it without using.

Point 2—Learn to Cope with Urges

Give some examples of basic coping strategies that you think might work for you and explain how you will use them.

_____

_____

_____

_____

_____

On the next page you will find an Urge Log. Many people tell us that they found great value in carrying this with them and making a note when they have an urge. A pocket notebook works well since it's easy to carry. We encourage you to fill it out for a period of time, then go back and see if there are patterns you can identify.

My Urge Log

Date	Time	Rate 1-10 Severity		Location	
	Length of urge	What triggered my urge?	Who was I with?	How I coped and my feelings about coping	Alternate activities, substitute behaviors

Point 2—Learn to Cope with Urges

Each time you manage to overcome an urge, the urge will return less often and less strong. Remember to put the PIG on a diet.

How will your Urge Log help you abstain from the behavior you don't want to do?

_____

_____

_____

_____

What does a slip on an Urge Log mean?

_____

_____

_____

_____

How effective will this tool be to help you achieve your goals?

_____

_____

_____

_____

Triggers for Urges

What is a trigger? Triggers are things that are so associated, in your own mind, with the addictive behavior that they lead to urges. They could be anything from walking past a familiar corner where you used to sell drugs, seeing any white powdery substance that reminds you of cocaine or an advertisement for alcoholic drinks. After a period of abstaining from addictive behavior, triggers slowly lose their association with the addictive behavior. Urges that result from triggers will usually subside quite quickly but may take many years to disappear completely.

Recognize your triggers:

To figure out your triggers, think about drugs or behaviors that stimulate your senses, such as seeing it, hearing it, smelling it, tasting it and touching it.

- Think about how the trigger affects your body, mind and behavior.
- Keep in mind that triggers are not unpredictable. You can see them coming.
- Make a list of these triggers; you may not be aware of how many there are.
- Keep track of how intense the triggers are for you; if you just "notice" urges without reacting to them they will become less intense.
- Keep track of how long they last; most people give in and don't realize that the effects of triggers don't last long, unless maybe if you stay exposed to them.
- Examples of possible triggers:
  » Heroin: needles, drug paraphernalia
  » Cocaine: white powder, tin foil, crack pipe, lighter
  » Alcohol: alcohol advertisements, bottles, sound of a can opening
  » Marijuana: music, pipes, rolling papers, vape machine
  » Drug Dealing: seeing a known dealer drive by in an expensive car
  » Car Theft: watching a robbery or mugging on TV
  » People: that you used with in the past

Write down a list of your triggers:

_____

_____

_____

_____

What is the difference between a trigger and an urge?

_____

_____

_____

_____

Point 2—Learn to Cope with Urges

Are triggers really powerful on their own or do we give them power by our beliefs?

_____

_____

_____

_____

Some people taking this course have said that a trigger is nothing but an excuse. What do you think?

_____

_____

_____

The Power of Habits

A habit is a regular practice, especially one that is hard to give up. When habits kick in, the brain can rest because it's not having to make decisions.

Researchers have identified what they call the **Habit Loop**. It starts with a *cue*, followed by a *routine* and a *reward*.

Habits are so powerful that they are almost impossible to break, but they *can* be changed. To do this, you use the same cue, but change the routine and find a new reward. New studies confirm that another key to changing a habit is belief; you have to believe you can change.

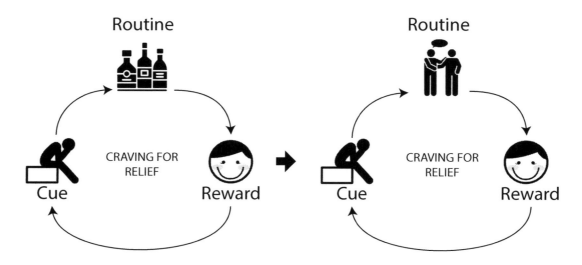

KEEP THE CUE
INSERT A NEW ROUTINE
ENJOY A NEW REWARD

On the first line, list a habit you would like to change, then follow it with a new routine and reward. Then repeat with another habit.

HABIT	CUE	NEW ROUTINE	REWARD
Ex: Smoking	Get in my car	Eat a piece of gum	Enjoy the flavor

Point 2—Learn to Cope with Urges

How can the knowledge of how habits work benefit people with addictive behaviors?

_____

_____

_____

_____

What have you learned in this course that convinces you that you can change?

_____

_____

_____

_____

Weekly Planner Explained

The most common situation where urges occur, as reported to us on urge logs, is boredom. Use the planner on the next page to fill your time with meaningful activities. We'll discuss this more later in the course. You need a plan for your time, your energy and your brain.

It is a fact, urges occur less frequently and with less intensity when you are engaged in physical or mental activity.

Point 2—Learn to Cope with Urges

Weekly Planner

Time	Monday	Tuesday	Wednesday	Thursday	Friday	Saturday	Sunday
Morning							
Midday							
Evening							

How can this tool help you abstain from the behavior you don't want to do?

How effective will this tool be to help you achieve your goals?

The ABC Tool

You have power to learn how to use tools to defeat urges, such as disputing irrational beliefs and verifying the thoughts that often cause them. Take bad ideas seriously and they lead you into dangerous situations. Learn to question your beliefs and take back control of your life.

The thoughts associated with addictive and criminal behaviors become automatic and we tend to act on these thoughts before we think through the consequences!

Such beliefs are often irrational; they are not accurate and do not help you achieve your long-term goals.

If you can identify and understand these irrational beliefs, you can choose to replace them with more rational or helpful beliefs.

Disputing Irrational Beliefs is a powerful tool to help in your recovery.

Activating event is what happened that set things in motion. If for instance your sister Pamela didn't come to visit like she said, which made you really angry, then "Pamela not coming to visit" is **A**—the activating event.

Belief is what you believe about the activating event. So the belief might be "she is doing something else and doesn't care about me anymore and this is unbearable and humiliating."

Consequence is how you feel, and then how you act as a result of what you believe about the event. So, Pamela no longer cares, has moved on with her life, and you think that is a humiliation, making you angry and upset. The ABC shows that how you feel depends on what you believe.

Dispute is what you can do to question your Beliefs. Ask yourself whether the Beliefs are true, rational and helpful to you. For example, do you know for a fact that she no longer cares and has moved on? Another word for dispute is verify.

Effective new belief is the new or rational belief you can use to replace the unhelpful one. By practicing this you can cope better with unpleasant events, even lowering the degree of how important it really is.

Start with **C**—the Consequence. Notice that you are furious or are having a terrible urge.

Then try to see what came before that, what the trigger was, the Activating event or **A**. Ask yourself "What happened to make me feel this way? Then try to work out your thoughts or **B**eliefs that meant this event had this effect on you. **D**ispute/Verify these beliefs, question them and decide whether they are true and helpful or irrational and unhelpful. If they are unhelpful, identify new healthy or **E**ffective beliefs to practice in the future to help you cope better.

My ABCs

Activating event	Belief about event— irrational	Consequence of my irrational belief	Dispute/verify my beliefs	Effective change in my thinking		
The event that set you off.	What I believe about A. Find the irrational demand—the MUST.	How I feel and how I behave as a result of B.	Were my thoughts helpful or unhelpful?	Is there a more balanced way of thinking about it?		
I was bored, needed excitement	Walmart guards are stupid, I won't get caught.	Arrested for shoplifting	I was wrong, they did catch me.	There are things I can do that won't lead to prison. I could have gone to the car show.		

You have power to learn how to use tools to defeat urges, such as disputing irrational beliefs and verifying the thoughts that often cause them. Take bad ideas seriously and they lead you into dangerous situations. Learn to question your beliefs and take back control of your life.

The thoughts associated with addictive and criminal behaviors become automatic and we tend to act on these thoughts before we think through the consequences!

Such beliefs are often irrational; they are not accurate and do not help you achieve your long-term goals.

If you can identify and understand these irrational beliefs, you can choose to replace them with more rational or helpful beliefs.

List several situations where you could use the ABC tool to figure out a better outcome

1) _____
2) _____
3) _____
4) _____

How does filling out this tool over and over again for different situations help you?

_____
_____
_____
_____

Verify, Verify, Verify

The 3 most important words in the English language are: **_Verify, Verify, Verify._** Why?

_____
_____
_____
_____

Point 3—Manage Thoughts, Feelings and Behavior

At the beginning of this book, we introduced you to REBT, the idea that your thoughts and beliefs create your experience—how you feel and how you act. Now let's look deeper into how our thoughts lead to our beliefs and then to our behavior.

Disputing Irrational Beliefs (DIBs)

You can use this tool to examine any belief that may be harmful if you act on it. For example, "I will just have one drink and then go home," or "I'll just flip these two packages for quick money, get out of the game and keep it moving." This could be true and make sense. But if, from your previous life experience, you see that this is very unlikely and will more likely lead to trouble with family or police, then this is not a rational belief.

An irrational belief (IB) is: Not true—it's unrealistic or there is no evidence to support it. Doesn't make sense—it's not logical. Harmful or unhelpful—it won't get you what you want for yourself in the long run if you act on it.

A rational belief (RB) is: True—it's realistic and there is evidence to support it. Makes sense—it's logical. Helpful—it helps you get what you want in the long run if you act on it.

You can dispute an irrational belief by turning it into a question and then answering it. Your answer will probably be a rational belief.

Example:

Irrational Belief: "I will just have 2 beers and then quit."

Question: "Will I just have just 2 beers and quit?"

Answer/Rational Belief: "Probably not, it's never worked in the past. If I have 2, the urge will be *greater* than if I don't have any."

Disputing Irrational Beliefs (DIBs)

List some negative thoughts you have had about yourself and others.

My irrational belief	Question my IB	My rational belief
I always fail.	Do I always fail?	I've failed in the past but I've had some successes as well

What is the Cause?

"I believe that my life is made up of 10% what happens to me and 90% how I react to it."

—Charles Swindoll, 2010

What is he saying and what does it say about the word *cause*?

_____

_____

_____

_____

"Humans do not get emotionally upset by events but by their thoughts about those events."

—Albert Ellis, 1958

What is he saying and what does it say about the word *cause*?

_____

_____

_____

_____

"There is nothing good or bad but thinking makes it so."

—William Shakespeare, *Hamlet* 1603

What is he saying and what does it say about the word *cause*?

_____

_____

_____

_____

*"Men are not disturbed by things
but by the views they take of them."*

—Epictetus, Greek slave born in Rome 85 AD

What is he saying and what does it say about the word *cause*?

_____

_____

_____

_____

*"You will continue to suffer if you have an emotional
reaction to everything that is said to you."*

—Bruce Lee

Is *cause* a legitimate excuse for our behavior?

_____

_____

_____

_____

Is reality *real,* or is it whatever you tell yourself it is?

_____

_____

_____

_____

"But" and *"because"* are two indicator words we can alert ourselves to and listen for. An example, "I love you but…" is not an expression of love and "I did that because…" generally occurs as a false justification. We have experienced for ourselves that almost "everything before but and after because is bullshit," as Charles True tells it.

Point 3—Manage Thoughts, Feelings and Behavior

Rewrite this sentence with an honest/accurate statement about what this person is saying, "Your happiness means more than anything to me but I need to use drugs to get through the day."

_____

_____

_____

_____

Remember this:
"You are always responsible for how you act,
no matter how you feel."

—Robert Tew

Is this an example of internal or external Locus of Control?

_____

_____

_____

How can we control how we feel?

_____

_____

_____

Reaction vs. Response

Irrational beliefs can be automatic. When you **react**, you are acting without considering the consequences; when you **respond**, you are making a reason-based decision that is in your own best interest. It is much better to respond than to react. The difference between a reaction and a response is the thought in between.

Responding allows you time to think about the right action, reflect on the beliefs driving and guiding the experience, and behave in a more informed and intelligent way.

How does this relate to the Locus of Control discussion?

_____

_____

_____

_____

Railroad Bob said,
"When you start to get that feeling,
just say j-j-j-j-j-a-a-a-a-i-i-i-i-i-l-l-l-l."

Why does he tell you to say that?

_____

_____

_____

List any changes you would like to make in your life

_____

_____

_____

"Growth is painful. Change is painful. But nothing is as
painful as staying stuck somewhere you don't belong."

—Mandy Hale

Point 3—Manage Thoughts, Feelings and Behavior

Unconditional Acceptance

In this course we'll guide you through techniques that can help you change your automatic thinking patterns. As you begin to think about the world differently, your emotions will change. Physically you will have less adrenaline in your blood, you won't feel flush, the fight or flight mechanism won't kick in and your behavior will change. Changed behavior will lead to better outcomes in your life.

Adopting unconditional acceptance can be a key to overcoming emotional problems associated with addictive behaviors. This also can be a life skill that will help you long after your addictive behavior is behind you. Unconditional acceptance is something we already know, but for it to become a personal philosophy you may have to learn to recognize the unhelpful beliefs you automatically hold when unpleasant or unexpected things happen in your life. Once you spot these in your thinking, you can remind yourself of more helpful ways to think.

This starts with reminding yourself that you are human. You know that you aren't perfect and that you'll make mistakes, do some things badly and do some bad things. This is all a part of being human, in that making mistakes and failing is how we learn.

When you find yourself automatically thinking negative thoughts, or exaggerating and judging how bad you are, remind yourself of your humanity and of those traits that we all share. By identifying unhelpful thoughts and replacing them with more accurate and helpful thoughts of acceptance, you'll feel better and want to act in healthier ways. After practicing this for a while, more accurate thinking will become automatic for you. Like most things though, it takes practice.

Unconditional Self-Acceptance (USA)

Unconditional Self-Acceptance is the idea that you have worth, just as you are. This explains what separates "you" from your behaviors. This is why SMART doesn't use labels. You may have addictive behaviors, but you are not an addict. You are a complex human being with many traits, some good, some bad. Labeling yourself with any *one* trait is just not true; it's not who you are.

Accepting yourself may be difficult. You may have caused yourself and others extreme harm and pain. But you can forgive yourself and accept that you are a worthwhile person in spite of your past behaviors.

Be patient with and kind to yourself. Be honest about what you've done. Accept that you can't change the past but you can create your future.

You may be tempted to compare yourself to others or hold yourself up to some arbitrary standard. There is no standard or universal measure of your value. Comparing yourself to others is as meaningless as comparing one color to another. Is red better than green?

Why is labeling yourself bad for you?

_____

_____

_____

_____

Unconditional Other Acceptance (UOA)

You may judge other people inaccurately or in an exaggerated way, just as you judge yourself. Once you accept that other people are capable of making mistakes, then you can accept that they may fail at things too. Judging another person as totally bad—no matter how badly they treated you—is as exaggerated and as harmful as making the same judgement about yourself.

Unconditional Life Acceptance (ULA)

You can judge life or the world in the same way, as being completely unfair or totally terrible. When you find yourself thinking, "life sucks, it isn't fair!" remind yourself of the good things that have happened in your life. If you will accept that there are many things that you can't control, it may help you to better accept what life throws at you, even if you don't like it.

List 5 good qualities about yourself.

1) _____

2) _____

3) _____

4) _____

5) _____

List 5 good qualities of someone who has wronged you.

1) _____

2) _____

3) _____

4) _____

5) _____

Tuition or Tragedy?

It is helpful to ask yourself, "Was the cost of my mistake tuition or tragedy?" If we learn from the mistake, we can call it tuition. It was the cost of learning what not to do. If we don't learn and repeat the mistake, and there is an additional cost without benefit, we say it is tragic.

Give an example of a mistake that you made that you would label as a "tragedy."

_____

_____

_____

_____

Give an example of a mistake that you made that you would label as "tuition."

_____

_____

_____

_____

Comparing Yourself to Others

Comparing yourself to others is usually a bad idea. You are comparing your inside to their outside. You're comparing how you feel about yourself on the inside to how they look on the outside. You have no idea how they really feel on the inside so it's not an accurate comparison.

Give an example of a time where you compared yourself to someone and the comparison could have been mistaken.

_____

_____

_____

_____

Rational and Irrational beliefs

Beliefs that people have about themselves and the world come in two categories:

1) Rational—They are true, make sense and are helpful.
2) Irrational—They are untrue, don't make sense and are harmful.

Common Types of Irrational Beliefs

Demands—*Must, have to* and *should* beliefs are absolutes that put unrealistic demands on you, others and life. "My wife must stop saying that to me."

Over-generalizations—*Only, always* and *never* beliefs also are absolutes—all or nothing—with no room for options. "I always screw up."

Frustration Intolerance—*I can't stand, I can't handle* and *I can't deal with* are generally false beliefs. "I can't deal with your nagging."

Awfulizations—*Worst thing ever, horrible, awful* and adjectives ending in *-est* (meanest, laziest, cruelest, etc.) "He's the meanest boss on earth."

Take time and ask yourself, Is this belief really true? What is the evidence to support it? Could there be another explanation for someone's behavior? What is a more balanced belief for what just happened?

Give an example of an irrational belief you have had about yourself:

_____
_____
_____
_____

What is a rational belief about yourself?

_____
_____
_____
_____

Give an example of an irrational belief you have had about someone else:

_____
_____
_____
_____
_____

Point 3—Manage Thoughts, Feelings and Behavior

What is a rational belief about that person?

_____

_____

_____

_____

Give an example of an irrational belief you have had about the world:

_____

_____

_____

_____

What is a rational belief about the world?

_____

_____

_____

_____

Words Matter

Strong emotions are an unavoidable part of being human, but you can reduce your stress by changing the words you use. Changing the words can lower your heart rate, blood pressure and anxiety level.

It would be better if you did not use the following words or phrases because they lead to irrational expectations. Beside each word write a sentence with that word. On the line below, write the sentence with a replacement word that will put less demand on the situation.

Must – I must get home before Christmas.

It would be nice if I got home before Christmas.

Should

_____

Have to

_____

Can't

_____

Ought to

_____

Awful

_____

Unbearable

_____

I am terribly anxious

_____

I am really angry

_____

Remember the 3 most important words in the English language: **verify, verify, verify!**

Thoughts, feelings, and actions: Which one lands you in jail?

_____

_____

_____

Point 3—Manage Thoughts, Feelings and Behavior

Criminal Thinking

People who commit crimes explain their behavior by telling themselves different reasons they are not to blame. Understanding these errors in thinking can help you choose not to participate in criminal and addictive behavior. There are many ways you have probably chosen not to take responsibility and blame someone or something else for your choices. See if you can find an example of yourself in these:

1) Continually point out inadequacies of the staff and/or others.
2) Build yourself up by putting others down.
3) Tell others what they want to hear and not what is true.
4) Lie—by omission, by distorting the truth and by disclosing only what benefits you.
5) Be deliberately vague. "Someone," "I'm not really sure," "Maybe," "If I feel like it."
6) Divert attention away from yourself. Introduce irrelevant material to confuse the situation.
7) Minimize the situation. "I just got into a little trouble." "It doesn't really make a difference."
8) Agree or say "yes" without really meaning it.
9) Pay attention only to what suits you.
10) Major on minors/Make a big scene about a minor point.
11) Put off responsibilities by saying, "I forgot."
12) Put others on the defensive. Use tactics such as degrading, quibbling over words, trying to embarrass, using anger as a weapon or using the love of others as a weapon.
13) Accuse others of misunderstanding.
14) Claim you have changed because you did it right once.
15) Gaslighting—a form of manipulation where you try to convince someone of something that they know isn't true by making them think they are crazy.
16) Bullying—the attempt to intimidate or aggressively dominate another person.

Give some example of criminal thinking you have heard or used in the past.

1)_____
2)_____
3)_____

Write an accurate, beneficial thought to replace the criminal thinking examples above.

1)_____
2)_____
3)_____

Thinking Errors

See if you can identify any of your own thinking that fits this pattern. Write down any thoughts you've had in the past that resemble these thinking errors.

Making excuses or blaming "If you grew up the way I did, you would have turned out the same way."

_____

_____

Doing nice things for people for selfish reasons You want something from someone so you do something nice for them thinking that they will then "owe you." You wash your mother's car then ask her to borrow it.

_____

_____

Entitlement (Believing the rules don't apply to you) "Rules are made to be broken. I deserve it so I'm taking it."

_____

_____

Power Orientation (Trying to control people) "Nobody tells me what to do. I'll tell you what to do."

_____

_____

Lazy Thinking (Looking for shortcuts) "I'm tired today, I'll look for a job tomorrow."

_____

_____

Cut-off (Getting rid of responsible thoughts) "It doesn't matter to me. I don't care what happens."

_____

_____

Deflection (Changing the subject to avoid admitting to a wrong or owning your behavior) "You got off work 3 hours ago, where have you been?" "I didn't know where you were for 4 hours yesterday."

_____

_____

Point 3—Manage Thoughts, Feelings and Behavior

Super-optimism (Feeling like you can get away with anything) "They're so stupid, they'll never find out or catch me."

_____

_____

Overgeneralization (Turning one event into something that always happens) "Every time you talk to me you are making excuses for something."

_____

_____

Negativity (Always putting a negative spin on things) "Hey, we're having a special dinner tonight" "Yes, but those always run late and I'll miss the first 30 minutes of my TV show."

_____

_____

Catastrophizing/Awfulizing "That's the rudest thing anyone's ever said to me!"

_____

_____

Fortune Telling (Predicting the future with certainty) "After that happens, I know what you'll do next...."

_____

_____

Mind Reading (Believing you know what someone else is thinking) "I can tell by that look that she thinks she's better than me."

_____

_____

Black and White Thinking (Refusing to hear someone's explanation or not being willing to consider the whole story) "You were late coming to visit me; I don't want to hear any more about it!"

_____

_____

Emotional Challenges

There are four significant emotional challenges that need to be addressed-
Anger, Stress, Thrill Seeking and Depression. Changing your thinking can improve your life.

Anger

We usually get angry when we generate some kind of agitation around *what we think about* what is happening. Anger can be positive if it energizes you to take action to benefit yourself. If it is destructive and causes you grief, it is negative and self-defeating. Long-term anger is unhealthy and can lead to high-risk situations linked to criminal and addictive behavior.

You can learn to stop/disrupt the irrational beliefs that make you angry, and instead control your behavior and reduce your risk of relapsing and returning to the criminal justice system.

We feel angry because of our *beliefs about situations.* ("We do not get upset by events but by our thoughts about those events." Albert Ellis)

Anger is just an emotion; it can feel overwhelming, but it does not make us act aggressively.

Aggression happens when we use our anger as an excuse to try to control or hurt other people.

Aggression is never inevitable and does not get us the things we most want out of life.

Learning to handle anger in a way that it does not become aggression is what will keep you out of the criminal justice system and in recovery.

Coping with anger is a choice you can make

Recognize the early warning signs of anger such as shakiness, muscle tightness, yelling or saying things that aren't true. Instead, try using one of the techniques below:

Take a break—Remind yourself that anger makes it hard to think clearly—there is always a risk of hasty and dangerous decisions when you are angry.

Remove yourself from the situation if you can. One moment's reflection can prevent you from violating your own healthy rights—and the rights of others.

Give yourself time to regroup, relax.

Treat the anger like an urge—a powerful emotion you can learn from but do not have to act upon.

Surf it like a wave—they roll in then pass.

Use mindfulness and practice acceptance.

Point 3—Manage Thoughts, Feelings and Behavior

Use rational beliefs such as: People have a right to act or to think or to feel as they wish, even if it is stupid. While I'd like to be treated fairly, there's no law of nature that says I must.

It is okay that I am feeling angry but I will make better decisions about what to do if I wait a while first and let these strong feelings subside.

How can you tell when your anger is building to an unhealthy level?

_____

_____

_____

_____

Which methods of coping with anger do you think might work for you?

_____

_____

_____

_____

"Self-control is strength; you have to get to a point where your mood doesn't shift based on the actions of someone else. Don't allow others to control the direction of your life."

—Morgan Freeman

How does Morgan Freeman's statement relate to the Locus of Control?

_____

_____

_____

_____

Anger Journal

Here is an example of how to use the ABC tool to manage your angry thoughts.

Write down situations where you felt anger and rate your mood from 1-10.

Write down what you were thinking about the situation at that time.

Then list evidence *for* and *against* the thought.

Write a more balanced thought, pause for it to sink in, then rate your mood.

Situation	Rate Mood	Automatic Thoughts	Evidence For	Evidence Against	Balanced Thought	Rate Again

Thrill-Seeking

When you take unnecessary risks with your life and your freedom such as shooting up, drinking into unconsciousness or doing things you know will put what you say you value in harm's way, you are thrill-seeking on some level. In other words, the characteristics of a thrill seeker are someone seeking change; who likes unusual, scary, surprising things; is unpredictable, likes the unexpected; is impulsive; takes risks without seeing danger or consequences; is rebellious; likes intense experiences.

It's like a gambler who knows they cannot win every hand but feels the need to risk it all each time they play.

What, if anything, have you done that sounds like thrill-seeking?

_____

_____

_____

_____

How can you change the Habit Loop with a healthier thrill-seeking behavior?

_____

_____

_____

_____

Stress

Stress is defined as a reaction of the body and mind to the mental and emotional strain placed on them. In life you experience stress every day.

Healthy Stress

In real life or death situations, stress is healthy and can give you the focus and strength to survive. Even in less serious situations, some stress is healthy and useful. Whether preparing for an exam, a sports contest, a job interview or a first date—the anticipation and just a little anxiety can help us take the situation seriously and focus on what we need to do. The important thing is that healthy stress helps you get things done rather than getting in the way. Think of stress like an alarm: it warns you to pay attention, you pay attention and the alarm then turns off. But what happens if the alarm does not turn off?

Unhealthy Stress

If you get chronically stressed, it is like an alarm that stays on even when there is no actual threat. Almost any situation is "read" by the brain as threatening so your whole body is constantly on high alert, ready to respond as if the world is always hostile, ready for fight or flight.

Consequences

Those stress chemicals working in your brain are perfectly safe in the short term but really bad for you if the alarm button is held down constantly.

Health effects: headaches, can't sleep, rashes, ulcers, dizziness, weakness, tiredness

Mental effects: nervous, bored, tired, can't concentrate, can't make decisions, irritable

Behavior effects: accident prone, take drugs and alcohol, restless, emotional outbursts, reduced range of behaviors (falling back on old habits)

Which consequences have you experienced?

_____

_____

_____

_____

Point 3—Manage Thoughts, Feelings and Behavior

Thinking Away Stress

Identify the stressors in your life: Watch out for the signs of stress, such as clenching your jaw, making fists, headaches, tension in your shoulders and neck, and feeling jumpy.

Change your attitude toward stress that you can't change: If you can't change it, try to understand, accept and cope with it.

Accept your limitations: Watch out for the demands in what you are thinking; the musts, shoulds, got-tos; and most of all do not put unrealistic expectations on things over which you have no control.

Worry constructively: Think about the situations you can control. Restrict your "worry time" and then work on a realistic plan to resolve the issue.

Don't sweat the small stuff: Richard Carlson wrote a whole book on the topic.

Look at your options: Don't jump into the first "solution" that pops into your head. Look for the *internal* Locus of Control option.

Defeating Stress with Mindfulness

Mindfulness is a way of training yourself to be more accepting of your own thoughts and emotions.

Remember that stressful thoughts are just that, thoughts. They are not you. Say to yourself, "Wow, that was a stressful thought!"

What will you try the next time you feel like you are getting stressed?

_____

_____

_____

_____

Depression

People with addictive behaviors may also feel sad, depressed or worried. In fact, alcohol is a depressant. Mind altering substances cause irrational thoughts and those thoughts can be a leading cause of depression. Changing your thinking can help you see situations more realistically, helping to relieve your depression, anxiety or worries. Sadness and depression are common occurrences in individuals with addictive behaviors. As with other emotions, what we think and believe makes a difference to depression, and so does social support.

Learning good coping strategies to handle feelings of sadness can help you avoid more serious depression.

Your feelings of sadness and depression depend on your thoughts and beliefs as well as your circumstances in life; you can learn to change the way you think and then feel better.

Depression is common in people who use alcohol and/or drugs. It may be one factor that **leads people to using** alcohol and/or drugs or **it may be a consequence of using** alcohol and/or drugs.

If you have suffered from depression, do you believe your depression led you to your use of substances or your use of substances led to your depression?

_____

_____

_____

_____

Managing Depression—Strategies that Work

Remind yourself that feelings pass.

Get Outside—Step outdoors for a few minutes to pull some weeds, sit in the sun or just get some fresh air.

Have a Laugh—Read a few pages of a funny book, watch a clip of your favorite comedian or call a friend who usually cracks you up.

Use Positive Self-Statements like "I've handled this before."

Take a Walk—A stroll around the neighborhood can lift your mood and bust stress.

Turn on Some Tunes—Put on something peppy, play a few of your favorite songs to relax and lighten your mood.

Connect—Call a friend to catch up, email a family member or text someone.

Do a Good Deed—Studies prove that when you show kindness to someone else, it makes you feel good.

Learn to say "No" to experiences that usually get you down.

Count What's Good—Pick up a pen and list a few things you're grateful for today. Think about your relationships, things that went well, and any positive parts of your life.

Get Physical—Do physical exercise (e.g., walking and running) at least three times a week.

Eat a Snack—Something that you will enjoy but keep it healthy.

Write a Thank You Note or Email—One study showed that people who did this actually felt more grateful.

Be Mindful—Realize your feelings for what they are, bad feelings or negative thoughts.

Meditate—Sit quietly, close your eyes and focus on your breathing.

Keep Busy—Engage in pleasurable activities or hobbies.

Choose Activities that give you a sense of achievement, even if they are not pleasurable (mow a lawn, wash a car).

Recognize the Things you Cannot Change and get on with the things that are worthwhile.

Wish Someone Well—Practicing compassion for others tends to make you feel better too.

Spend Time with Friends, don't isolate yourself.

Go to SMART Recovery or other mutual aid meetings.

Spend Time Helping other People—it will help you more than you can imagine!

Check a Chore off your List—What is a small chore you have been meaning to do? The satisfaction of getting it done could lessen your stress.

Practice your Faith whatever it is, read your book.

A Course for Successful Life Skills

Write down additional ideas that you have:

_____

_____

_____

_____

Write down three strategies you will use to manage depression:

_____

_____

_____

_____

What do negative feelings, urges and boners all have in common?

_____

_____

_____

_____

We spend a lot of time in this book talking about our thoughts and how they make us feel. we have learned to dispute irrational beliefs and not to let our behaviors define who are. Why is this so important? Many of our beliefs about ourselves, others and the world lead to frustration, fear and anger. When our reality makes us feel bad, what's the quickest way to feel good?

_____

_____

Is that a long term or short term solution?

_____

Give examples of a long-term solution to feeling bad.

_____

_____

_____

Point 4—Finding Balance in Life

What does a balanced life look like?

In order to live a balanced life, you want to find the right proportions, or *balance,* for the things you spend your time doing. You will find that balance brings you a sense of peace and significantly reduces your stress level and anxiety. Here are a few areas to consider:

Work—Satisfaction, a feeling of accomplishment and pride are all positive feelings that can come from an honest day's work.

Play—We want to plan time to do the things we enjoy. This may even include *healthy* thrill-seeking activities like we discussed in an earlier lesson.

Rest—Adequate rest and sleep are vital if we want to be successful with the rest of our activities. Quiet and downtime allow us to refocus our attention on what's important to us.

Exercise—It's a fact, a sedentary body does not feel good! It gets stiff and sore and lacks energy. Movement of almost any kind gets our blood pumping and makes us feel better. Exercise will help you sleep better, manage your weight and increase your energy.

Explore Learning—Learning something new stimulates our brains which, similar to a muscle, makes them healthier and more productive.

Giving Back—We all have many things we can give: our time, money, love, support, encouragement and sharing our knowledge are just a few that will make you feel good about yourself.

Building Relationships—Quality relationships don't just happen on their own. If you want a good friend, you have to spend time *being* a good friend. Spending quality time with friends and family helps you build your own personal support group.

Spirituality—Do you believe in something? Anything? What do you hope for? Think about it and write it down for your own peace of mind.

Creating—This isn't just for artists; anyone can create a plan to accomplish something, decorate a room, take a road trip, get a job. The opportunities are endless.

Dreaming—It's healthy and productive to spend some time dreaming of a positive future. If you can't picture it in your mind, odds are it's never going to happen.

Personal Finances—You won't be at peace if you spend more money than you make. Living with a balanced budget is usually essential to living a balanced life.

Personal Growth—You may want to allocate some time to work on your full recovery.

What else is important that you do?

_____

_____

_____

_____

List the top 5 areas of your life and explain why they are important to you.

1) _____

2) _____

3) _____

4) _____

5) _____

_____

_____

_____

_____

_____

_____

_____

Balanced Life—How Do I Do It?

Here are some suggestions:

Eat Well—After you stop an addictive behavior, you may find that your appetite returns. Healthy eating and maintaining a balanced diet are essential to good living.

Get Some Exercise—Regular exercise can work wonders for your health and well-being. A 30-minute walk five days a week, for example, has been shown in research to *reverse the effects of depression for many people.*

Sleep—Many people with addictive behaviors have very irregular sleep patterns and sleep can change dramatically when a person stops drinking or using drugs. Getting your sleep patterns back can really help your emotional health.

Connect with Others—People who build strong networks of friends and acquaintances who are not involved in addictive behavior are much more likely to be successful in their recovery. *Social isolation hugely increases the risk of relapse* back to all those old behaviors.

Give Something Back—People who get into the habit of giving something back to other people or their local communities really do feel better about themselves. They tend to get depressed less, have fewer health problems and are happier!

Be Mindful—Many people recovering from addictive behaviors find themselves preoccupied with thoughts about the past or future, or get caught up with strong feelings such as urges. Learning to pay attention to the present moment and becoming more "mindful" can improve well-being and lifestyle balance.

Manage Your Emotional Life—Strong emotions are an inevitable part of the human condition. Using SMART tools can help you manage extreme emotions better.

Journal—Research suggests that humans form thoughts at the rate of 1000-3000 words per minute! They come to us from all parts of our brain at once from our past, present and our imagination. Writing your thoughts down forces you to put them into sentences, and gives you a chance to verify them and determine if they are truly rational or not.

Make a Plan—You know you are going to run into people who will ask you why you're not drinking so figure out now what you are going to say. You know you will have unexpected expenses, so make a budget and a plan to save. You may have relationships that you want to repair and one conversation won't change things; make a plan to repair the damage.

Looking at pages 67-69, what new activities and suggestions can you add?

_____

_____

_____

_____

A Course for Successful Life Skills

Looking at pages 67-69, which appeal to you the most? How will you use them?

1) _____

_____

2) _____

_____

3) _____

_____

4) _____

_____

5) _____

_____

Lifestyle Balance Pie—Measuring Satisfaction

Think of your life as a pie, divide it into slices and then label each piece with an area of your life that is important to you, *e.g.,* family, friends, spirituality, romance, health, work, recreation, personal growth, learning, giving back, etc.

Within each slice, draw another line as a ruler. Think of the pie's outer edge as being completely satisfied (10) and the center as being totally dissatisfied (0). Give a rating to your level of satisfaction in each of the areas you've listed by placing a dot to indicate the level of satisfaction you have in each particular area of your life.

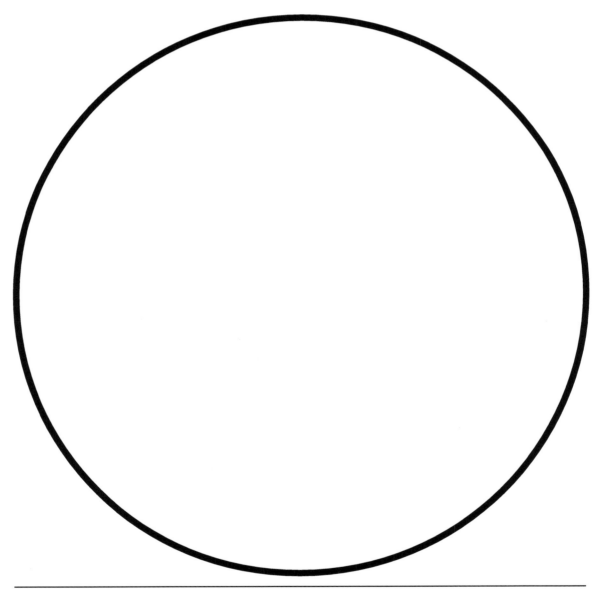

After rating each slice, connect the dots to create a new outside perimeter of your pie. What does it look like? Is it round and full, and ready to put on the table for everyone to see? Or does it look like bites have been taken out of it?

Write your answers to the following questions:

Am I living a balanced life?

_____

_____

_____

_____

Am I involved in too many activities? Is there too much on my plate?

_____

_____

_____

_____

Are there areas of my life that need more of my attention?

_____

_____

_____

_____

SMART Goals

It's common for people to set a result as their goal. I want to lose 20 pounds, have a dental checkup with no cavities, reconnect with my sister, etc. These are all results of many smaller steps. SMART Goals are very helpful for the steps to get to your larger goal.

Once you've chosen a result to work toward, think about the smaller steps you need to get to that result. You don't necessarily have to think any further out than your next step, although listing all the steps you can think of could be a good first SMART Goal.

Specific: Exactly what are you going to do? Who will you do this with? Where are you going to do this?

Measurable: How many? How often? How much? How will you define "complete"?

Attainable: Is this actually possible? Do you have everything you need?

Realistic: Is this too big of a step to do all at once? On a scale of 1-10, how confident are you that you can accomplish this? If your confidence level is less than 6, how can you adjust your plan so you can be more confident?

Timeframe: Exactly when are you going to do this or when will you declare this period complete?

Set yourself up for success. Set small, attainable goals and congratulate yourself when you've accomplished each one. If you discover your goal wasn't actually attainable, congratulate yourself for learning something and adjust or change your goal to be more realistic. Try to avoid planning to do something every day – it's more motivating to accomplish more than you set out to do than to feel like you failed for missing one day out of seven.

Consider setting yourself a weekly self-care SMART Goal as well. What is one small thing can you do for yourself this week that would be helpful for your state of mind, your well-being, or your recovery?

Keeping a record of your completed tasks can help you see the progress you've made toward your SMART Goals!

SMART Goal Setting

Now that you have identified areas of your life that you want to upgrade, let's set some goals.

Life category (from Lifestyle Balance Pie):_____

Related to value (from Hierarchy of Values-HOV):_____

Goal:				
Is it **S**pecific	How will you **M**easure it	Is it **A**ttainable	Is it **R**ealistic	What is the **T**imeframe
Tasks to reach goal 1:				
Specific?	Measure?	Attainable?	Realistic?	Timeframe?
Tasks to reach goal 2:				
Specific?	Measure?	Attainable?	Realistic?	Timeframe?
Tasks to reach goal 3:				
Specific?	Measure?	Attainable?	Realistic?	Timeframe?

Relapse Prevention: Activities

ARTS—Cartooning, Drawing, Lettering, Mechanical Drawing, Painting, Photography.

CHORES, USEFUL TASKS—Cleaning House, Clean the Garage, Cooking, Yardwork, Gardening, Car Repair, Fence Building, Wash a Car, Detail a Car, Polish a Car, Build a Shed, Paint a Room.

EXERCISES—Running, Jogging, Stretching or Cardio Exercises, Skipping Rope, Yoga, Weightlifting, Join a Gym.

FOOD ACTIVITIES—Baking, Cooking, Barbecuing, Learning how to prepare and eat healthy meals.

GAMES—Video games, Dominos, Puzzles, Monopoly, Poker, Scrabble, Crosswords, Sudoku.

HANDICRAFT ACTIVITIES—Picture Framing, Woodworking, Furniture Re-finishing, Carving, Lathe Turning, DIY projects, Learn and Practice Magic Tricks.

LEARN SOMETHING NEW—Absolutely anything you want to learn how to do can be found on Pinterest.com or YouTube.com.

MARTIAL ARTS—Aikido, Jujitsu, Judo, Karate, Fencing, Wrestling, Boxing.

OUTDOOR ACTIVITIES—Gardening, Crabbing, Fishing, Canoeing, Sailing, Hunting, Skiing, Swimming, Archery, Hiking, Hatchet Throwing, Car Shows, R/C Cars, Boats, Planes.

PEER-TO-PEER GROUPS—Go to several to find one that you really like; start a new meeting with the help of friends.

PERFORMING ARTS—Dancing, Singing, Play an Instrument, Join a band.

PERSONAL GROWTH—Self-help Books, Workshops, Lectures, Meditate, Career Development, On-line Courses, ***Become a SMART Recovery Facilitator***. Churches, Community Centers, Museums and City Government all sponsor lectures and events. There are clubs in major cities for all sorts of special interests.

READING—Fiction, Novels, Plays, Poems, Nonfiction. There is a magazine for every special interest under the sun. Join a Book Club.

SOCIALIZING ACTIVITIES—Attending or Giving Parties, Rap Sessions, Political Events. There are many Outdoor Festivals for music, art, dance, food, antiques. Go to a Livestock Auction, Antique Car Auction, Neighborhood Association Meeting.

SPECTATING—Watching Movies, Plays, Sports, Pageants, Rodeo.

SPIRITUALITY—If you're not sure what you believe, think about it and figure it out. Then study and learn more about your choices.

SPORTS—Join a league, Baseball, Basketball, Golf, Bowling, Fantasy Football, Dancing, Tennis, Running, Shoot Pool.

STUDYING ACADEMIC SUBJECTS—Art, History, Language, Math, Music, Science, Social Science, Anthropology—the study of humans and how we developed, such as

How were the Pyramids in Egypt built, Psychology, Sociology, Astronomy—How the Universe works.

TRADES AND CRAFTS—Bricklayer, Builder, Carpenter, House Framing, Welding, Landscaping, Mechanic, Machinist, Law Enforcement, Dog Training, Knife Making.

THRILL-SEEKING—Bungee Jumping, Ziplining, Public Speaking—Toastmasters, Horseback riding.

VOLUNTEER—Church, Hospitals, Recovery Centers. Do you have and elderly family member or neighbor? Offer to take them to a doctor appointment or the grocery store.

WRITING—Journal, write a short story, report on an event.

Many of these involve other people and can be a great bonding opportunity to build your support network.

What can you add to this list that you like to do?

_____

_____

_____

_____

How important is it to find something that interests you and pursue it? Explain

_____

_____

_____

_____

Never be a prisoner of your past.
It was a lesson, not a life sentence.

—Unknown

Point 4—Finding Balance in Life

Weekly Planner

You previously wrote down what was important to you on your Lifestyle Balance pie, then rated your level of satisfaction. Next, you set goals to "balance your pie." Now we are going to take it to the next step and put it on our calendar.

Time	Monday	Tuesday	Wednesday	Thursday	Friday	Saturday	Sunday
Morning							
Midday							
Evening							

Tips: Look at the previous pages for suggestions. Plan your activities to avoid triggers and to hang out with people who support your commitment to your recovery. Filling your time with fun and productive activities can be one of your best strategies to avoid relapsing. Isolating is probably the worst thing you can do and for many people it's their first choice. Why do people tend to isolate?

_____

_____

A Course for Successful Life Skills

Many of the items on your list will cost money, so let's make a simple budget.
Be sure to add additional expenses that you may have.

Monthly Budget Template for month of _____		
	Estimate	Actual
Item	Estimate	Actual
Salary 1		
Salary 2		
Other		
Other		
Other		
Total		
Item	Estimate	Actual
Rent		
Car Loan		
Car Insurance		
Clothing		
Food		
Childcare		
Utilities		
Healthcare		
Cell Phone		
Charity		
Internet		
Cable		
Gifts		
Restaurants		
Entertainment		
Savings for Goal 1		
Savings for Goal 2		
Savings for Cash Reserves		
Savings for Retirement		
Total		

Monthly Budget Template for month of _____		
Income vs. Expenses		
Item	Estimate	Actual
Monthly Income		
Monthly Expenses		
Difference		

Congratulations! You have just completed a detailed plan that uses the power that you have to improve your life.

Note: Your budget must be redone every month. Managing money to a goal is a moving target; you must constantly re-aim. Income changes; your hours may be cut or you may get overtime. Expenses increase and you will find new places to save. Adjust your estimates every month to account for changes.

Consequences of Credit Cards on Your Budget

Store #1—You go to a store where all items are marked with the prices. It's not on the price tag but understood that when you pay at the register you will be charged an additional 8.25% sales tax on the items you bought.

$100 worth of merchandise costs you $108.25

Store #2—You go to a store where all items are marked with the prices. It's not on the price tag but understood that when you pay at the register you will be charged an additional 8.25% sales tax on the items you bought. This store also charges an additional 20% (or more) on top of the marked price *and* the sales tax. There is no sign stating this.

$100 worth of merchandise costs you $129.84, or $155.81 after 24 months.

Where are you going to shop?

If you pay with a credit card and don't pay off the balance, you are shopping at store #2 every time you spend your money.

> *"You don't have a money problem, you have a spending problem!"*
>
> —Dr. Phil

How do you overcome this obstacle to living a low stress balanced life?

_____

_____

_____

How do you balance enjoying it now vs. saving for later?

_____

_____

_____

> *"The quickest way to double your money is to fold it over and put it back in your pocket."*
>
> —Will Rogers

Point 4—Finding Balance in Life

*"Don't save what is left after spending,
spend what is left after saving."*

—Warren Buffett

The way you make more money is make yourself more valuable to the people and organizations that you work for.

If you filled out your budget and made a plan for all the expenses a responsible person has today, including savings for unexpected things that pop up, insurance for items that you cannot afford to replace if they are lost, and money for you and your family's future, odds are you could use more resources. Most people want at least enough money to *participate comfortably in society*. For me, that means that my basic needs for food, shelter and access to healthcare are met and secure. It also means I can buy someone a gift, donate to charity, go to an occasional sporting event and get to work if my car breaks down.

What does *participate comfortably* in society mean to you?

_____

_____

_____

Let's start by looking at the definition of Job and Career according to the dictionary.

Job—"A task or work that one is paid for." Most businesses have jobs that need to be done. Martin Luther King Jr. said, "Whatever your life's work is, do it well." A job, any job, can be a source of pride, satisfaction and income.

However, many *jobs* are not considered one of the key ingredients that makes a company successful; they just have to be done. Jobs are sometimes automated with technology like software programs or a new machine. In a fast-changing world, many jobs are not secure for the long-term.

Career—"A job with opportunities for progress." Having a career implies that you have employment and seek a bigger job, based on your experience, with more responsibility and higher pay.

One is not better than the other but it's important to understand which one you are working on.

A Course for Successful Life Skills

What jobs have you had in the past?

_____

_____

_____

What job would you like to try in the future?

_____

_____

_____

How to Make More Money!

Employee #1—He wants to be given a job and left alone to do it. *He* decides how much effort he will give, based on the pay and how much work *he* thinks the company deserves. When something goes wrong, he blames others; he's never made a mistake. He knows exactly how many minutes late for work he can be without getting called out and uses it every day just due to his feeling that he can get away with it. He believes people treat him unfairly and no one gives him a break. He loves office gossip and talking about other people's problems. He believes he's smarter and knows more than anyone else, especially his boss.

Employee #2—He wants to be an essential part of a company's success. He talks to everyone he can about the business (while working) to better understand what the company is trying to accomplish. He does his job and helps others get their work done. When he's walking from his car in the morning, he stops and picks up a piece of trash in the parking lot, when no one even sees him, and throws it away. He gets to work early enough to get coffee, talk to his buddies about last night's game and get to his post ready to work on time. He refuses to listen to gossip about co-workers' personal lives. He wants to know how everything works because the more he knows, the more he can do to help.

He lets his bosses know that he wants to move up in the company and is willing to do the work to get there. He always behaves in a professional manner.

If you own a business, you have your money invested and your family's future is at stake, which one would you hire, promote or give a raise to and why?

_____

_____

_____

We are all working on a building project. I go to nail up a board and realize I cut it too short. Joe, who is sitting on his ass watching, says, "Look at that dumbass, he cut the board too short."

What do you think about me?

_____

_____

_____

What do you think about Joe?

_____

_____

_____

_____

List 10 things that you can do to earn the respect of your co-workers and boss that ***do not*** involve education, experience or natural talent:

1) Be on time_____
2) _____
3) _____
4) _____
5) _____
6) _____
7) _____
8) _____
9) _____
10) _____

Top 10 Job Interview Questions

How useful is roleplay in getting ready for any interview?

How useful is it for us to put ourselves in other people's shoes?

How will you now answer these questions?

Tell me about yourself.

_____
_____
_____
_____

Why do you want to work here?

_____
_____
_____

Why should I hire you?

_____
_____
_____
_____

Point 4—Finding Balance in Life

Where do you see yourself in 5 years?

_____

_____

_____

_____

Tell me about a problem you had at work in the past and how you dealt with it.

_____

_____

_____

_____

What are your salary requirements?

_____

_____

_____

_____

Why are you changing jobs?

_____

_____

_____

_____

Why did you leave your last job?

_____

_____

_____

_____

Tell me a success story about your last job, something you did really well?

_____

_____

_____

_____

Do you have any questions for me?

_____

_____

_____

_____

What will you tell or not tell them about your incarceration?

(Hint: Honesty is the best policy. Do you like being lied to? The truth will set you free. Never lie, it doesn't work.)

_____

_____

_____

_____

> *"It's not who you think you are that holds you back,*
> *it's who you think you're not."*
>
> —Denis Waitley

What does he mean by that?

_____

_____

_____

_____

Improve Your Social Support Network

Your recovery journey will be much more challenging if you hang around with people still involved with addiction and criminality. Almost as risky is becoming isolated and having no friends. We all need support, we all need friends, and if we are lucky, we will still have family that supports us as well. Even when you have burned all of your bridges you can still build a strong network based on the vision you have for changing your life right now.

Rate how much you agree with these statements on a scale of 1-10 (1-strongly disagree, 10-totally agree) then explain why.

Being around friends who are still involved in addiction is a huge risk to my recovery.

_____

_____

_____

Being around friends who are supportive of my abstinence but still using is a huge risk to my recovery.

_____

_____

_____

Being isolated is a huge risk to my recovery.

_____

_____

_____

Building a network of friends who are not involved in addiction makes it much more likely that my recovery will be successful.

_____

_____

_____

_____

It is really hard to walk away from people just because they are too risky to be around.

_____

_____

_____

_____

At the end of the day, it is easier than spending another year in jail?

_____

_____

_____

_____

Our social support networks might best include people who know about recovery or are in recovery themselves.

_____

_____

_____

_____

Lessons from Geese

This autumn, when you see geese heading south for the winter and flying along in a "V" formation, you might consider what science has discovered as to why they fly that way. As each bird flaps its wings, it creates "uplift" for the bird immediately following. By flying in a "V" formation, the whole flock adds at least 70% greater flying range than if each bird flew on its own.

People who share a common direction and sense of community can get to where they are going more quickly and easily because they are travelling on the thrust of each other. When a goose falls out of formation, it suddenly feels the drag and resistance of trying to go it alone and quickly gets back into formation to take advantage of the lifting power of the bird in front.

If we have as much sense as a goose, we will stay in formation with those who are headed in the same way that we are.

When the lead goose gets tired, it rotates back in the wing and another goose flies point. It is sensible to take turns doing demanding jobs with people or with geese flying south. Geese honk from behind to encourage those up front to keep up their speed. Finally, and this is important: when a goose gets sick or is wounded by gunshots and falls out of formation, two other geese fall out with that goose and follow it down to lend a helping hand and for protection. They stay with the fallen goose until it is able to fly or until it dies. Only then do they launch out on their own or with another formation to catch up with their group.

If we had the sense of a goose, we would stand by each other like that.

– From a speech given by Angeles Arrien

The idea that humans are stronger together than by themselves is as old as humanity. Who will you rely upon for strength as you move forward? Be specific.

_____

_____

_____

_____

Examine Unhealthy Relationships

If you want to know what a person believes, take a look at the people with whom they associate and where they live. Ending close relationships is difficult and takes a great deal of courage; it's much easier to isolate. However, if your friends are taking part in certain addictive and/or criminal behaviors, then they are unhealthy for you to be around. You may need to explain to them why the relationship cannot continue (which may also get them to look at their own behavior). Still remember, **you cannot change anyone!** Prepare for this meeting in advance and make sure to meet in a safe place. Acknowledge to yourself that it might be a painful loss. If this is the case, get help, take someone who is supportive of your new goals with you.

Are there any relationships in your life that are unhealthy? If so, how will you plan for them?

_____
_____
_____
_____

How will you handle an unhealthy relationship if it's someone close like your wife or brother?

_____
_____
_____
_____

What will you tell your close friends about the changes you are making in your life?

_____
_____
_____
_____

What will you tell your family about the changes you are making in your life?

_____
_____
_____
_____

Point 4—Finding Balance in Life

What type of new people do you need in your life?

_____

_____

_____

_____

New Friends

There will be a strong pull toward spending time with old friends who take part in your old addictive behavior. Making new friends is not easy, but it is necessary for protecting your recovery.

Here are some suggestions for making new friends:

Risk rejection by reaching out and making contact, take the first steps towards positive people.

Suggest that the person join you in doing something casual like going out for a cup of coffee or joining other friends who are planning to do something together. Suggest to someone that you meet at a peer group meeting you've heard about.

Have realistic expectations. People sometimes say no when you ask them to do something. They may be available at another time or they may not be interested. Such responses are part of a normal social life that we want to learn to accept. Be patient, many people have good reasons to be cautious.

How you will go about explaining to your old friends that you have changed your lifestyle?

_____

_____

_____

_____

How you will go about making new friends?

_____

_____

_____

_____

Learn to Deal with High-Risk Situations

It is easier to deal with situations that might trigger relapses or lead to criminal behavior by having multiple skills to use:

Talk Through It: Build a social support network and use it!

Walk Through It: Role-play and rehearsal are like stretching and drills; they increase the odds of success and safety on the field of play.

Think Through It: Is it true; does it sound rational; is it helpful; will it help me achieve my goals?

Balance Lifestyle: Increase pleasant activities, use relaxation training or meditation, use your balance life plan and goals (for example, work and time with family).

Cope with Urges: Identify your triggers, *have a plan* for the situations that you know are going to happen.

Plan ahead: You know that you will have to face certain people, places and situations. Don't be caught off guard; make a plan and rehearse it.

Attitude—Inside vs. Outside

Relationships between people involved in offending are often based on power and control.

People who show kindness or manners in prison may be seen as weak, but this is *normal behavior in the real world*—and more likely to help you get what you really want in the long term.

If you can shake off the offending culture and ways of thinking, you are much more likely to get what you want out of life in the long term—and stay out of the criminal justice system for good!

Which of these ideas do you think could help you be successful?

_____

_____

_____

_____

SMART Recovery Activities:

Plans, Behaviors, Thoughts, Coping Strategies, Beliefs

SMART Recovery—Plans

Make a plan and rehearse it in your head. You know that people are going to ask you about your abstinence; don't be caught off guard. Identify your triggers and have a plan to deal with them. You know that using isn't working well for you and you want to stop. You have to fill that time, the space in your brain and in your heart with something else. Make a plan!

SMART Recovery—Behaviors

Attend SMART Recovery and other peer group meetings. Plan to attend _____ times per week.

Review this book, *A Course for Successful Life Skills,* and update your answers on a regular basis. Purchase a copy of the InsideOut Handbook and read it for more detailed information.

Recognize Triggers that lead to using, including social pressure, interpersonal conflict, external cues (people, places, situations), internal cues (hungry, thirsty, tired), and strong emotions (anger, sadness, loneliness, frustration).

Use urge-controlling techniques, such as riding-the-wave, delay, distract, mindfulness, meditation and review my cost-benefit analysis.

Recognize that my thoughts, emotions, and behaviors are related, and that *the words I choose to use* matter.

Recognize and try to *reduce my self-destructive behaviors*.

Work toward progress, not toward perfection. I can accept myself unconditionally.

Seek long-term satisfactions in my life. Participate in healthy and meaningful activities.

SMART Recovery—Healthy Thoughts

I am not powerless over my drinking/drugging.

I recognize that relapse is part of recovery and that each lapse, should it occur, is a learning opportunity.

I can pause to think before I act on my thoughts and emotions, thus leading to a better outcome.

I can recognize the difference between my thoughts, feelings and behaviors, and can change my beliefs that contributed to my drinking/using, for example, the "shoulds" and "musts" in my life.

SMART Recovery—Coping Strategies

I recognize that my feelings pass eventually; I can tolerate uncomfortable feelings, recognizing them as a normal part of everyday living.

I can reach out to others and ask for help.

I have SMART Recovery tools *(such as coping statements and the ABCs)* to help manage my thoughts and emotions, and my reactions to them.

List the SMART Recovery activities that might be helpful to you and explain how you will use them.

1) _____

_____

2) _____

_____

3) _____

_____

4) _____

_____

5) _____

_____

SMART Recovery Beliefs: Nurturing Hope

I now believe that:

I can acknowledge my mistakes and hold myself accountable, knowing that change is possible.

I have value to others, and I can share my experiences with them.

I can live a healthier, more satisfying life.

I can learn to stop thoughts of helplessness, hopelessness, and low self-worth.

I can reach out and grab the potential that life has to offer, being fully aware and present.

I can share my SMART Recovery plans with loved ones, so they can see what I am getting out of my recovery program.

According to research, what % of people stop using with no treatment or help of any kind?____%

Handling Lapses and Relapses

Now let's consider what you can do if you lapse or relapse. Lapses usually do occur, so it's a very good idea to be prepared in advance to deal with them.

Remember, *FAIL* stands for **F**irst **A**ttempt **I**n **L**earning.

A *lapse* is defined as a time when you take a drink or may even drink heavily one night, but then you stop.

A *relapse* is when you continue to use for two days or longer.

The following five steps will help you to avoid changing a lapse into a relapse:

1) **Review what happened.** Use your ABC Tool (p. 40) for this purpose—and if you go to a group, discuss it with them. Use your lapse as a learning experience—you can learn from your mistakes.

2) **Condemn the drinking behavior, but don't condemn yourself or make yourself feel guilty or ashamed.** It is your behavior that you want to change. It's appropriate for you to feel very irritated and very concerned with your experiences; after all, you have failed to live up to an important commitment you made to yourself. But it does not mean that you are a failure as a human being.

3) **Be careful that you don't go to the other extreme and minimize what happened.** For example, if you say to yourself something like: "The lesson says I shouldn't feel bad about relapsing. I'm not a terrible person. I just have to try again," you are partly correct. You are not a terrible person. The behavior was bad, however, and probably harmful to you and to your relationships

4) **Avoid telling yourself something foolish like: "Well, I've screwed up now, so I might as well have another."** Stopping at any time is always better than continuing. It is possible to stop in the middle of a drink.

5) **Don't label yourself as a failure or a loser or a hopeless person.** Labels such as these are overgeneralizations. You do thousands of things in any given week—some good, some bad. It would be far more helpful to say to yourself something like, "I did screw up. I did fail to keep my commitment to myself not to drink. But it doesn't make me a failure. It means that I need to practice even harder to prevent myself from relapsing again."

Recovery Definition:

A process of change through which individuals improve their health and wellness, live self-directed lives and strive to reach their full potential.

Relapses and lapses are NOT part of the SMART program of change.

They can be useful educational experiences if you analyze in detail how and why they occurred. When you make a mistake, and you will, due to the fact that you are human, ask yourself, was it tuition or tragedy? If you learned something from the experience, it's tuition, the cost of learning. If you didn't learn from your mistake and choose to make the same one again, that's a tragedy.

It does not mean you are a failure; it shows that your recovery plan and support system need to be strengthened.

You did not lose all your chips; before the relapse you went a long stretch without using or drinking, and that proves that **you are capable of living free of the addiction.**

Urges are weak and short-lived, and they grow weaker over time. In fact, after six months of abstinence, they can become fleeting thoughts or you seldom even think about them.

There is no such thing as error-free learning. Failure is a necessary component to any learning experience. What to do? Revise your plan and try again; try to learn from your mistakes so you don't make them again.

When Thomas Edison was inventing the light bulb, he tested over 1,000 materials for the filament before finding one that worked. He didn't fail 1,000 times, he discovered 1,000 materials that didn't work before finding the one that did. Some people make many attempts at sobriety; each one is a learning experience that gets them closer to their goals.

Write down those things you have learned about yourself when you were trying to change a behavior that wasn't working well for you.

1) _____

_____

2) _____

_____

3) _____

_____

Where I will get support

For each situation below, list up to two people you can call or places you can go for help and support.

You just learned you lost your job.

_____

_____

You want to celebrate your birthday.

_____

_____

You are nervous about a job interview.

_____

_____

You feel stressed from a bad day.

_____

_____

You feel like drinking or using drugs.

_____

_____

Identify at least two people who support your abstinence and who are willing to support your efforts to change:

_____

_____

Where will I start to build a solid support network?

_____

_____

Who can I review my goals for a Balanced Life with?

_____

_____

Point 4—Finding Balance in Life

Mindfulness

"a state of mind that we get to by focusing on the present moment, while calmly, without judgment, accepting our thoughts, feelings and body sensations."

Mindfulness has been practiced for several thousand years and is growing in popularity today. Research studies have consistently shown a positive relationship between mindfulness practice and mental health. It is used today to reduce symptoms of depression, to reduce stress and anxiety and in the treatment of drug addiction.

Negative thoughts affect how we feel and how we feel affects our behavior. It helps to recognize negative thoughts for what they are, thoughts. Researchers claim that our brain is capable of creating up to 3,000 words per minute!

A brain just like yours and mine conceived the great pyramids of Egypt, put a man on the moon, can be hilariously funny, creates total nonsense and can produce absolute terror. We don't have to become every thought that passes through our minds.

Some people find it easy to recognize negative thoughts and immediately put them to the test before acting: Is it true, rational and helpful?

"Hmm, I'm having an unbearable craving. Is it unbearable? No. Is it unpleasant? Yes. Can I get through it? Yes, I've done it many times before."

"He disrespected me. I need to show him by…" What he said did seem rude; was it intentional? I wonder what's bothering him today; I know it wasn't anything I did. "Maybe his ole lady fed him brussels sprouts again last night," LOL.

Name it to Tame it. When we give a name to how we are feeling, we give ourselves a little space between the feeling and ourselves. It gives us a chance to recognize that we are dealing with something rather than allowing it to overwhelm us or become us.

Think of a name for your thoughts to use so that when it happens, you can say to yourself, "I see _____ is back trying to get me in trouble again."

Give an example of an unpleasant thought you've had that you can recognize as a thought and not who you are.

_____

_____

_____

How would you dispute or verify that thought?

_____

_____

_____

Meditation

"the act of giving your attention to only one thing."

Meditation is a tool that helps you learn to work better with your mind. It will give you better focus and attention and help you feel more relaxed and calm. Begin by sitting in a comfortable chair with your back straight but not stiff and your arms relaxed in your lap. You want to focus on one thing such as your breathing. Other thoughts will come into your head, that's OK; your mind is creative and wants to be heard. Gently but firmly remind yourself of your breathing. When your mind wanders off again, bring it back. That's perfectly normal. Practice this for 5 minutes to begin with. As you become better at it, that is your mind learns to stay focused, you may find you can meditate for 20-30 minutes. I find it easiest to listen to a guided meditation on YouTube.

Go to youtube.com and you will find many of them to choose from, or try the one on the next page

Point 4—Finding Balance in Life

Meditation

Meditation has been around for thousands of years and is more popular today than it's ever been. It's a great way to relax and relieve stress.

Start by placing both feet in front of you on the floor, place your hands facing up in your lap and close your eyes.

Sit very still and focus on your breathing. Feel the air go into and out of your lungs. Notice your belly button rise when you inhale and go down when you exhale. Breath with your belly muscles. Inhale… exhale.

Focus on how your body feels. Inhale… exhale.

Thoughts will come and go, that's normal, just bring it back to focus on your breathing, inhale… exhale.

Starting with your toes, I want you to tighten them… then relax. As you release each set of muscles, imagine your stress floating away with it. Tighten your feet… relax… and release the tension. Tighten your ankles… relax. Tighten your calves… relax. Tighten your thighs… relax. Tighten your butt… relax. Feel the tension leaving your body. Inhale… exhale. Tighten your stomach… relax. Inhale… exhale. Tighten your hands… relax. Tighten your forearms… relax. Tighten your shoulders… relax. Inhale… exhale. Inhale… exhale. You should feel very relaxed. Inhale… exhale.

Picture yourself lying on the beach…. Listen to the waves…. They roll in… then roll out…. Feel the warmth of the sun on your skin. Smell the salty water…. Inhale… exhale.

Stretch out your legs and arms, reach as far as you can. Inhale… exhale. Now relax and open your eyes.

Explain what changes, if any, you experience in your body and mind after meditating.

_____

_____

_____

_____

Your diet is not only what you eat. It is what you watch, what you listen to, what you read, the people you hang around... be mindful of the things you put into your body emotionally, spiritually and physically.

Name: _____

Date: _____

Locus of Control Survey

____1. Do you believe that most problems will solve themselves if you just don't fool with them?

____2. Do you believe that you can stop yourself from catching a cold?

____3. Are some people just born lucky?

____4. Most or the time, do you feel that getting good grades means a lot to you?

____5. Are you often blamed for things that aren't your fault?

____6. Do you believe that if somebody studies hard enough, they can pass any subject?

____7. Do you believe that most of the time it doesn't pay to try hard because things never turn out right anyway?

____8. Do you feel that if things start out well in the morning that it's going to be a good day no matter what else you do?

____9. Do you feel that most of the time parents listen to what their children have to say?

____10. Do you believe that wishing can make good things happen?

____11. When you get punished does it usually seem it's for no good reason?

____12. Do you find it's hard to change a friend's opinion about something?

____13. Do you think that cheering more than others helps a team to win?

____14. Do you feel that it's nearly impossible to change your parents' mind about anything?

____15. Do you believe that parents should allow children to make most of their own decisions?

____16. Do you feel that when you do something wrong, there's very little you can do to make it right?

____17. Do you believe that most people are just born good at sports?

____18. Are most of the other people your age stronger than you are?

____19. Do you feel that one of the best ways to handle most problems is to just not think about them?

____20. Do you feel that you have a lot of choice in deciding who your friends are?

Fold and tear here

____21. If you found a 4-leaf clover, do you believe that it might bring you good luck?

____22. Do you often feel that whether or not you do your homework has little to do with the grades you get?

____23. Do you feel that when someone is angry at you, there is little you can do to stop them?

____24. Have you ever had a good luck charm?

____25. Do you believe that whether or not people like you depends on how you act?

____26. Do your parents usually help you if you ask them to?

____27. Have you felt that when someone is angry with you it is usually for no reason at all?

____28. Do you feel that you can change what might happen tomorrow by what you do today?

____29. Do you feel that when bad things are going to happen, they are just going to happen no matter what you do to try to stop them?

____30. Do you feel that people can get their own way if they just keep trying?

____31. Most of the time, do you find it useless to try to get your own way at home?

____32. Do you feel that when good things happen, they happen because of hard work?

____33. Do you feel that when someone wants to be your enemy, there is little you can do to change their mind?

____34. Do you feel that it's easy to get friends to do what you want them to do?

____35. Do you feel that you have little to say about what you get to eat at home?

____36. Do you feel that when someone doesn't like you, there is little you can do about it?

____37. Do you feel that it's useless to try hard at work or school because other people are just plain smarter than you?

____38. Do you believe that planning ahead makes things turn out better?

____39. Do you feel that you usually have little to say about what your family decides to do?

____40. Do you feel that it's better to be smart than lucky?

Point 4—Finding Balance in Life

Evaluation Form

Name:_____

Rate the value to you of each lesson on a scale from 1-10 with 1 being no value and 10 being great value.

_____ REBT

_____ Locus of Control

_____ Hula Hoop Theory

_____ Cost Benefit Analysis

_____ Problem of Instant Gratification

_____ Believe It You Can Change

_____ Treatment or Recovery

_____ Recovery Capital

_____ SMART 4-point Program

_____ Hierarchy of Values

_____ Change Plan Work Sheet

_____ Strategies for Coping with Urges

_____ Urge Log

_____ Triggers for Urges

_____ Power of Habits

_____ Weekly Planner

_____ ABC Tool

_____ Verify, Verify, Verify

_____ Disputing Irrational Beliefs

_____ What is Cause?

_____ Life is 10% what happens to me and 90% how I react to it

_____ Unconditional Acceptance

_____ Tuition or Tragedy

_____ Criminal Thinking

_____ Thinking Errors

_____ Anger

_____ Thrill Seeking

_____ Stress

_____ Depression

_____ Balance Life

_____ Lifestyle Balance Pie

_____ SMART Goal Setting

_____ Relapse Prevention Activities

_____ Consequences of Credit Cards

_____ How to Make More Money

_____ Social Support Network

_____ Lessons From Geese

_____ Examine Unhealthy Relationships

_____ High Risk Situations

_____ SMART Recovery Activities

_____ SMART Beliefs

_____ Handling a Lapse

_____ Where to Get Support

_____ Mindfulness

_____ Meditation

Will you give us a quote on the value of this course that we may use?

_____

_____

_____

_____

_____

_____

What did you really get out of the course?

_____

_____

_____

_____

_____

_____

_____

_____

_____

How can we improve; what can we do better?

_____

_____

_____

_____

_____

_____

_____

_____

Fold and tear here

106

Conclusion

You have here a lot of ideas and techniques for overcoming addictive behavior and irrational thoughts and beliefs. It's important to remember that when you first try to do something differently it feels awkward and uncomfortable—in fact, it may even feel "wrong" in some way. Plus, at first you usually don't do new things very well. You make mistakes. It will be very helpful if you accept this fact of life: new ways of thinking and behaving are going to feel awkward at first. And at first you may not do them very effectively.

On the other hand, if you avoid doing things that are new, awkward, and uncomfortable, you're probably going to be more likely to relapse. Remember that, even if you wish it were true, you're probably not so special and unique that once off alcohol or drugs you'll never have the urge to drink again. What's true for other people is probably true for you. It is important to prepare yourself in advance for the discomfort and for the fact that it's going to take some time for you to get the gist of your new routine.

It may be very helpful for you to join a group. If you asked someone to build a house for you and he insisted on doing it himself, what would you think about him? That he's a nut, right? Why do you think it is best to do this difficult job alone? If you get ten people to help you build your house, it's likely to done more quickly and efficiently.

Six Guidelines for Success

1) Try to maximize both your short-range pleasures and your long-range pleasures, and to achieve a balance between the two.
2) Remember that doing what is in your best interest may sometimes mean doing what is in someone else's best interest, and that this is likely to take practice.
3) Accept yourself even with your idiosyncrasies, failings and past mistakes. Condemn your foolish or poor behavior, but not yourself.
4) Remember that this same principle applies to others as well: they may do stupid or unfair things, but they, too, are fallible human beings and not awful people who should be shot!
5) Try not to awfulize or catastrophize about bad events or situations, since that will only make matters worse. The reality is "it is what it is."
6) Practice taking responsibility for your own emotional life.

Writing things down can be very helpful, especially at the beginning. If you try to do all of this new thinking in your head, you may get very confused. Even if you don't like filling in forms, it will probably help you change more effectively if you do so.

Reading self-help pamphlets and books will also help you. So seek them out and use them. But most of all, practice reviewing and rehearsing. Learn from your successes and failures, and prepare today for troublesome triggers tomorrow.

NOTES

_____
_____
_____
_____
_____
_____
_____
_____
_____
_____
_____
_____
_____
_____
_____
_____
_____
_____
_____
_____
_____
_____
_____
_____
_____
_____
_____
_____
_____
_____

APPENDIX

LOCUS of CONTROL SURVEY SCORING SHEET

These are NOT correct answers, and if you don't match, you are NOT WRONG.

Use this sheet to score your LOC survey and find out if your thinking leans more toward internal or external locus of control.

Count the number of matches and write the number here: _____

_Y_1. Do you believe that most problems will solve themselves if you just don't fool with them?

_N_2. Do you believe that you can stop yourself from catching a cold?

_Y_3. Are some people just born lucky?

_N_4. Most or the time, do you feel that getting good grades means a lot to you?

_Y_5. Are you often blamed for things that aren't your fault?

_N_6. Do you believe that if somebody studies hard enough, they can pass any subject?

_Y_7. Do you believe that most of the time it doesn't pay to try hard because things never turn out right anyway?

_Y_8. Do you feel that if things start out well in the morning that it's going to be a good day no matter what else you do?

_N_9. Do you feel that most of the time parents listen to what their children have to say?

_Y_10. Do you believe that wishing can make good things happen?

_Y_11. When you get punished does it usually seem it's for no good reason?

_Y_12. Do you find it's hard to change a friend's opinion about something?

_N_13. Do you think that cheering more than others helps a team to win?

_Y_14. Do you feel that it's nearly impossible to change your parents mind about anything?

_N_15. Do you believe that parents should allow children to make most of their own decisions?

_Y_16. Do you feel that when you do something wrong, there's very little you can do to make it right?

_Y_17. Do you believe that most people are just born good at sports?

_Y_18. Are most of the other people your age stronger than you are?

_Y_19. Do you feel that one of the best ways to handle most problems is to just not think about them?

_N_20. Do you feel that you have a lot of choice in deciding whom your friends are?

_Y_21. If you found a 4 leaf clover, do you believe that it might bring you good luck?

_N_22. Do you often feel that whether or not you do your homework has little to do with the grades you get?

_Y_23. Do you feel that when someone is angry at you, there is little you can do to stop them?

_Y_24. Have you ever had a good luck charm?

_N_25. Do you believe that whether or not people like you depends on how you act?

_N_26. Do your parents usually help you if you ask them to?

_Y_27. Have you felt that when someone is angry with you it is usually for no reason at all?

_N_28. Do you feel that you can change what might happen tomorrow by what you do today?

_Y_29. Do you feel that when bad things are going to happen, they are just going to happen no matter what you do to try to stop them?

_N_30. Do you feel that people can get their own way if they just keep trying?

_Y_31. Most of the time, do you find it useless to try to get your own way at home?

_N_32. Do you feel that when good things happen, they happen because of hard work?

_Y_33. Do you feel that when someone wants to be your enemy, there is little you can do to change their mind?

_N_34. Do you feel that it's easy to get friends to do what you want them to do?

_Y_35. Do you feel that you have little to say about what you get to eat at home?

_Y_36. Do you feel that when someone doesn't like you, there is little you can do about it.

_Y_37. Do you feel that it's useless to try hard at work or school because other people are just plain smarter than you?

_N_38. Do you believe that planning ahead makes things turn out better?

_Y_39. Do you feel that you usually have little to say about what your family decides to do?

_N_40. Do you feel that it's better to be smart than lucky?

Locus of Control Scoring Scale

0-6 matching answers

High Internal Locus of Control: You have a firm belief in your ability to determine your outcomes in life. You can influence what happens to you. A low score is associated with a relatively high stress tolerance.

7-15 matching answers

Mixed Locus of Control: You do believe that you do have control over your fate in some areas of your life, while believing that you have little control in others.

16 or more matching answers

High External Locus of Control: You have a fairly strong belief that events in your life are beyond your control. In other words, you do not feel that there is much of a connection between your behavior and your outcomes. You tend to believe that success and failure are primarily a matter of luck and chance. A high score is associated with a relatively high level of stress.

Is there anything you can do to change your outlook on life?

_____

_____

_____

_____

113

Made in United States
Orlando, FL
26 October 2024

53133996R00067